Agro Information System:
Identification and Parameterization of Needs of Farmers, Planners and Research Workers

P. S. Metkewar
Senior Consultant
Zensar Technologies Ltd.
ALPS Building, AN3/H2
Kharadi Campus, Pune - 14, INDIA

H.S. Acharya
Head
Department of Basic Sciences and Computer Technology
College of Agricultural Engineering
Marathwada Agricultural University
Parbhani - 431 402 INDIA

International Book Distributing Co.
(Publishing Division)

Published by

INTERNATIONAL BOOK DISTRIBUTING CO.
(Publishing Division)
Chaman Studio Building, 2nd Floor,
Charbagh, Lucknow 226 004 U.P. (INDIA)
Tel. : Off. : 2450004, 2450007, 2459058 Fax : 0522-2458629
E-Mail : ibdco@sancharnet.in

First Edition 2006

ISBN 81-8189-149-X

Composed & Designed at :

Panacea Computers
3rd Floor, Agrawal Sabha Bhawan
Subhash Mohal, Sadar Cantt. Lucknow-226 002
Phone : 0522-2483312, 9335927082
E-mail : prasgupt@rediffmail.com

Printed at:

Salasar Imaging Systems
C-7/5, Lawrence Road Industrial Area
Delhi - 110 035
Tel. : 011-27185653, 9810064311

Preface

This book presents a study of Agricultural Information System with the view to identify the problems of design and implementation. This book has been divided into eight chapters.

The first chapter is devoted to the general introduction to the subject matter. Agriculture is the oldest and most important vocation of the world. Integrated electronic databases, or any designed integrated on-line information system for use of farmers, agricultural planners, administrators and agricultural marketing people are not available in this country at this point of time.

Agricultural sector has its own requirement of 'Information System' like industry or defence. Planning and implementing an agricultural information system even for any defined geographic region would require basic information of various components like hardware requirements, software requirements, need of the user and policies of the implementing agencies namely government agricultural departments etc.

The second chapter is devoted to problem identification where the need for an Agro Information System is emphasized.

Chapter three contains details of System analysis conducted. Specifically logistics, data flow diagrams, data dictionary have been provided with respect to subsystems like Agricultural marketing, Irrigation. System analysis of Research and education have also been presented.

Chapter four is devoted for discussion on design of an Information system. Criteria for selection of hardware, communication media have been initially presented and then detailed discussion on application software to meet specific needs is given. Exclusive section on special tools is incorporated, where details of search engines, statistical tools, simulators and Geographic Information System tools are discussed.

Chapter fifth, sixth, seventh and eight are devoted to specific subsystems like farm-advisory, Agricultural Marketing, irrigation, research and education. Though these four systems do not cover the whole of the Agro Information System, these have been presented here because they are singularly important.

The Analysis and Information presented in this book should be useful to network based online information system designers, planners and administrators taking care of farm activities alike.

P. S. Metkewar

H.S. Acharya

Acknowledgements

A famous writer has rightly written of the importance of making a good beginning. For me too, this came true with Dr. H. S. Acharya as my research supervisor. It was he who encouraged me and reached me to the heights I stand today. In him I have always found a heart of a guardian, brain of a scientist and warmth of a friend. I shall always admire his art of envisaging Computer Science. Though this little eulogy is not enough to express my deep sense of gratitude towards him, my everlasting regards goes out to him.

I owe a word of thanks to my friend Mr. Nitin Tamboli for his useful discussions, valuable suggestions and remarkable research inputs during the course of this investigation.

I would also like to thank the Director, Prakash Khanale and teaching and the non-teaching staff of Computer department, Institute of Information Technology and Management, Parbhani for their timely assistance and overwhelming support during my entire course of research.

I would also like to offer my heartful regards to the teaching and non-teaching staff of Computer department, M.G.M. College of C.S. & I.T., Parbhani for their great help.

I extend my affectionate thanks to my close friends Syed Khizer, Rajesh Walse, Avinash Chitnis and Omprakash Arya and also to my other friends for their sincere friendship, moral support and co-operation during the course of my research.

I can hardly find words to express my deep sense of gratitude towards my loving father Shri. Satyanarayan Sayanna Metkewar and cherished Mother Shakuntala Satyanarayan Metkewar for their gracious blessings and affection that helped me to make my task a cheerful one.

I would also like to thank my beloved sisters Rajashri, Ranjana and Rupali and Brother-in-law Shri. Shankar H. Karampuri and other family members whose constant love, support and encouragement has been the main force behind my work and will also continue in the days to come.

P. S. Metkewar

Contents

Chapter 1 : Introduction **1**
1.1 Literature Survey 3
1.2 Websites and Portals 5
1.3 Objectives of the current study 5
1.4 Organization of the Chapters 6

Chapter 2 : Problem Identification **9**
2.0 Introduction 9
2.1 Need and perpetuality: 9
2.2 Sources and attributes of existing information system 13
2.3 Inadequacy of current information system 16
2.4 Information Technology (IT) based information system as possible solution: 17

Chapter 3 : System Analysis **21**
3.0 Introduction 21
3.1 System Analysis: Methodology 21
3.1.1 The Survey 22
3.1.2 The Secondary Data: 23
3.2 Targeted geographic area and targeted users: 23
3.3 Modes of dissemination of Information 27
3.3.1 Electronic media: 27
3.3.2 Direct communication 35
3.3.3 Print media 36
3.4 Information Generation /Production Mechanisms and agencies. 37
3.4.1 Information for Farming 37
3.4.2 Information for Marketing and finance 40
3.4.3 Information for Agro - industrial activities 44
3.4.4 Information for Seed industries 44
3.4.5 Information for Fertilizer Industries 45
3.4.6 Information for Pesticide and Insecticide industries 46

3.4.7 Information on weather and soils, suitability of soils 47
3.4.8 Information on Irrigation Projects and water availability 49
3.4.9 Information for Research and Education 50
3.4.10 Information on area, production and productivity 52
3.5 The Dynamics: information flow diagrams 52
3.6 The Data Mining Concepts 54
3.7 Agencies/Organizations Established with the mandate for Data mining 54

Chapter 4 : Design of an Information System 61
4.0 Introduction 61
4.1 Definition of Agro Information System 61
4.2 Different models of AIS 64
4.3 Procedure of Design specifications 1 and 2 67
4.4 Procedure of Design specifications 3 and 4 70
4.5 Procedure of Design specification 5 76
4.6 Tools room 77
4.7 Client / Server model 79
4.8 Special techniques: 83
4.8.1 Leased line 83
4.8.2 Smart card Technology 84
4.8.3 Unicode Technology 85
4.8.4 Virtual Private Network technology 87
4.8.5 Middleware concepts 88
4.9 Interfacing techniques 89
4.10 Some useful concept for System Manager 91

Chapter 5 : Farm - Advisory Subsystem 93
5.0 Introduction 93
5.1 Suggested models 94
5.2 Information content 94
5.3 Description of components of static information 95
5.4 Description of components of dynamic pages 96

5.5 A prototype of Self Upgrading Advisory Tool for Extension. 101
5.6 Icon based query formation tool or Search Engine with keyword search: 112
5.7 Indian language processing capabilities 114
5.8 Voice Recognition Software 117

Chapter 6 : Agricultural Marketing Subsystem 119

6.0 Introduction 119
6.1 Agriculture Market website 120
6.2 Suggested models 120
6.3 Information content 122
6.4 Description of components of static information 123
6.5 Description of components of dynamic pages 124
6.6 Requirement specification 125
6.6.1 Farmer module 126
6.6.2 Commission Agent module 127
6.6.3 Traders module 130
6.6.4 APMC organization module 131
6.6.5 APMC information outlet module 135
6.7 Regulated Agricultural Market viewed as Neural Nework 135

Chapter 7 : Irrigation Subsystem 145

7.0 Introduction 145
7.1 Irrigation related websites 146
7.2 Suggested Design specifications 146
7.3 Data Warehousing Strategies 147
7.4 Information content 148
7.5 Utilities of the contents item by item 150
7.6 Expert System on Irrigation 151

Chapter 8 : Research and Education Subsystem 153

8.0 Introduction 153
8.1 Website of ICAR organizations SAU's 154
8.2 Suggested models 157
8.3 Information content 157

8.4 Design of static information 158
8.5 Design of components of dynamic pages 159
8.6 Subject grouping and relevant keywords 159
8.7 Virtual Library 160
8.8 Virtual University 161
8.9 Virtual Classrooms 162
8.10 Web enabled Simulated Experiment (Virtual Lab) 163

Chapter 9 : Conclusions 165

Appendices

Appendix 1 : Sample code of Farm - Advisory system 167
Appendix 2 : Sixty-four states and Stability of the crop 189
Definitions: 191
Acronyms 192
References 195
Index 201

List of Tables

Serial No. **Name of Table** **Page No.**

1. Table 2.1: Information received by farmers through mass media 10
2. Table 2.2
   a) Sources of farm information and measures of their differential use: Regional rankings 10
   b) Sources of farm information: International Rankings (a 14-state survey in U.S. –1984) 11
3. Table 2.3: Extent of needs of training of T&V worker 11
4. Table 2.4: Measures of Gap in knowledge: (in percentage) 13
5. Table 2.5: Major advantages and disadvantages of different channels: 14
6. Table 2.6: Evaluation of Doordarshan by farmers as a source of information 15
7. Table 2.7: Evaluation of Radio as a source of information by farmers 15
8. Table 2.8: Relative credibility different sources of information perceived by farmers 15
9. Table 3.1: Distribution of the Informants for the System analysis 23
10. Table 3.2: Population distribution of Marathwada region by profession: 24
11. Table 3.3: T&V workers, research worker and students of agricultural schools and colleges: 25
12. Table 3.4: Locations of Radio stations and Their coverage in Marathwada 28
13. Table 3.5: List of Agricultural programmes on radio 28
14. Table 3.6: BSNL stations and its allotted number of connections 30
15. Table 3.7: Farm related web sites: 31

16. Table 3.8: Estimated distribution of the farmers who use farm journals and popular newspapers statistics 36
17. Table 3.9: Measure of effectiveness of knowledge gained after reading agricultural information from newspapers 36
18. Table 3.10: List of Agricultural colleges and Research stations in Marathwada region 38
19. Table 3.11: List of Seed agencies 39
20. Table 3.12: Name / URLs of consumer organization / NGOs 40
21. Table 3.13: Show distances in-between the markets 42
22. Table 3.14 : Logistics of MMCs and SMCs 43
23. Table 3.15: Name of financial institutions in Marathwada 43
24. Table 3.16: List of Fertilizer agencies: 45
25. Table 3.17: List of Insecticide or Pesticide agencies 46
26. Table 3.18: V-SAT Numbers : 47
27. Table 3.19: Major, Medium and Minor irrigation projects 49
28. Table 4.1: Comparison between existing communication channel of radio and television station and what it should be in Information Technology (IT) based system 62
29. Table 4.2: Comparison between existing communication of extension worker & farmer and what it should be in IT enabled system 63
30. Table 4.3: Comparison between display of charts & posters and what it should be in IT enabled system 63
31. Table 4.4: Comparison between training to extension worker and what it should be in IT enabled system 63
32. Table 4.5: Comparison between seminar or conference or workshop and what it should be in IT enabled system: 64

33. Table 4.6: Comparison between print media and what it should be in IT enabled system: 64
34. Table 4.7: List of recent CPU availability 68
35. Table 4.8: Classification of interconnected processors by scale 72
36. Table 4.9: Various factors or attributes for comparing the major media 72
37. Table 4.10: Operating system and its corresponding web servers: 74
38. Table 4.11: List of Security software (Firewall softwares) 75
39. Table 5.1: Decision Table of Extension Information Subsystem 105
40. Table 5.2: Structure of the ans_table. 103
41. Table 5.3: The structure of the adv_faqs table. 103
42. Table 5.4: The structure of the passwd table. 104
43. Table 5.5: The structure of the statistics table. 104
44. Table 5.6: The structure of the user_id table. 105
45. Table 5.7: The structure of the words table. 105
46. Table 5.8: List of Marathi software's and its fonts 114
47. Table 5.9: Primary keyword 115
48. Table 5.10: Secondary keyword 115
49. Table 5.11: Information generator keyword 115
50. Table 6.1: Name of the markets, crops and year of data. 141
51. Table 6.2: A typical Asymptotic stable case of State 45 in case of Tur 143
52. Table 6.3: Co-efficient of variation in the considered crops 144
53. Table 7.1: Design specifications on Irrigation 146
54. Table 7.2: Data warehouse requirement 148
55. Table 8.1: List of portals and website of ICAR institutions and the SAU's. 154

List of figures

Serial No.	Name of Figure	Page No.
1.	Figure 3.1: Organizational chart of Agricultural Produce Market Committee (APMC):	42
2.	Figure 3.2: Organizational chart of State Department of Irrigation (SDI)	50
3.	Figure 3.3: Information flow diagram of State Department of Irrigation	51
4.	Figure 3.4: Decision diagram of process of allocation of water for farmers involving only one divisional and one sub-divisional office	52
5.	Figure 3.5: Organizational chart of Marathwada Agricultural University, Parbhani	53
6.	Figure 3.6: Programme production and telecasting.	55
7.	Figure 3.7: Cycle of programme generation, broadcasting and feedback.	56
8.	Figure 3.8: Possibilities of information flow through Internet.	57
9.	Figure 3.9: Information flow diagram of T&V system	58
10.	Figure 3.10: Information Flow diagram of APMC:	59
11.	Figure 3.11: Decision Flow diagram of farmer	60
12.	Figure 4.1: Leased line connection	71
13.	Figure 4.2: Connection of VSAT	71
14.	Figure 5.1: Data flow diagram of Question - Answer system	106
15.	Figure 5.2: System flowchart of Farmer - System Interface	107
16.	Figure 5.3: System flowchart of Extension Officer - System Interface:	108
17.	Figure 5.4: Farmer - System Interface with a DFD:	109
18.	Figure 5.5: Extension Officer - System Interface with a DFD	110
19.	Figure 5.6: Layout structure of database	103
20.	Figure 5.7 : Specimen of Soil Testing form.	97

21. Figure 5.8: on-line or instant chat with Extension expert: ... 100
22. Figure 5.9: Data flow diagram of icon based query formation tool or search engine: ... 113
23. Figure 6.1: Different channels of Agricultural Marketing ... 121
24. Figure 6.2: Client - Server architecture of controlled marketing system. ... 121
25. Figure 6.3: Markets are continuously communicating with each other: ... 138
26. Figure 6.4: Synapse generated by Unsupervised learning method. ... 143
27. Figure 7.1: Players in the Irrigation Expert system. ... 151

List of Maps

Serial No. **Name of Map** **Page No.**

1. Map 1 : Location of Radio stations and their coverage. 29
2. Map 2 : Location of Doordarshan stations and their coverage. 29
3. Map 3 : Marathwada Region - Targeted area 26
4. Map 4: Research and Educational institutions. (For Agril. Schools: refer Table 3.10) 41
5. Map 5 : Agro-climatic Zones of Marathwada Region 99

Chapter 1
Introduction

Agriculture is the oldest and most important avocation of the world. Agricultural sector has its own requirement of 'Information System' like industry or defense. Planning and implementing an agricultural information system even for any defined geographic region would require basic information of various components like hardware requirements, software requirements, need of the user and policies of the implementing agencies namely government agricultural departments etc.

Integrated electronic databases, or any designed integrated on-line information systems for use of farmers, agricultural planners, administrators and agricultural marketing people are not available in this country at this point of time. Even the scenario in developed countries is not much different. Some databases, however are available. For example, AGRICOLA of United States Department of Agriculture, and AGRIS, developed by publishers of CAB ABSTRACTS (Naber G., 1994) are two databases providing information to scientists and farmers.

Information strategies for agriculture have been the concern of policy makers and planners for quite some time. Considerable manpower employed at the cost of the taxpayer's money, is engaged in generating meaningful information for the benefit of farmers, Agro-processors, Marketiers, Extension workers, Financiers, Research workers, Administrators and Students in this country. They have been working for decades now. Because of the geographical extent of this very large country the man-power engaged in production of information is employed in organizations separated by thousands of kilometers. Most of these sites are in rural areas. A major challenge in the first decade of the new millennium is to organize these resources into more coherent, properly connected and sharable systems. Evidences of cooperation of international institutes and premier national agricultural research organizations in Asia towards efficient information management strategies, which are on since 1993 (Mook, 2001), are strong indicators of the fact that much is required to be done in the area of information management for agriculture.

At the bottom, the level of farming itself, the size of the problem can be seen to be huge. It is stated in one of the policy papers (Alam, 2001) that 143 million ha of net area is cultivated in India, distributed over 115 million land holdings out of which nearly three fourths of the holding are in the range of 1-2 ha size (small and marginal holdings). These are with people who are generally poor; they face capital and management constraints. These people require proper information and decision support systems as their managerial skills are low. Currently these requirements are met through traditional methods of agricultural extension, supported by Central and State Governments. Information and communication management has been on the agenda of Indian Council and Agricultural Research (ICAR) as evidenced by efforts taken under various projects. ARPIS (AgriculturalResearch Personnel Information System), ARFIS (Agricultural Research Financial Information System), ARMIS (Agricultural Research Management Information System) and ICAR home page (http//www.nic.in/icar) are few examples of such projects.

It is also generally claimed that National Agricultural Research System (NARS) of India is one of the three largest R&D research networks in the world (Alam, 2001), with about 25,000 research workers, extension workers actively engaged in production and dissemination of agricultural information. ICAR with the help of National Centre of Software Technology (NCST), has been instrumental in building up an Agricultural Research Information System (ARIS) over the past decade. Creation of databases, digitized documents, Internet connectivity, and seamless communication between scientists has been some of the contents of the action plan of ARIS.

The fertilizer companies, the seed companies, the sugarcane growers cooperatives, state seed certification agencies, irrigation departments, the meteorological department, soil survey agencies, water resource development organizations, agricultural planning and price commissions, regulated market committees and many more agencies are also engaged in production and dissemination of information relevant to agriculture.

Reasons why in spite of efforts from many, the current scenario in this particular direction is not all satisfactory could be many. Keeping this problem in mind we have taken up this study entitled: "Agro information system: identification and parameterization of needs of farmers, planners and research workers."

In its crudest form an agro information system may be represented pictorially as

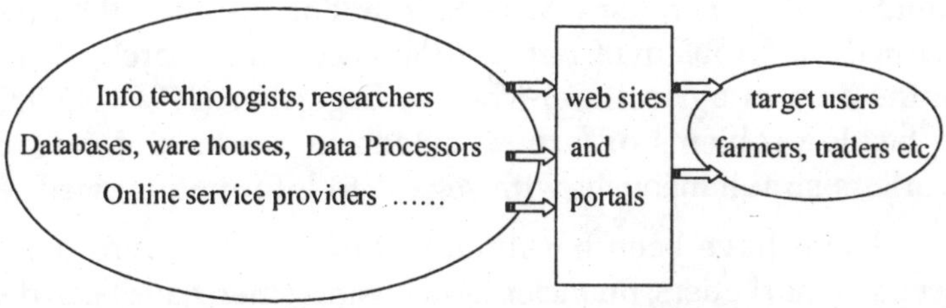

Because of this there is a general tendency to consider information systems synonymous to portals and web sites. This is not true. An information system is much more than a portal. Defining an information system unambiguously is a very difficult task. Hence we propose to project a clear picture of an information system specific to the field of agriculture, through parameterization.

1.1 Literature Survey

Many research workers have conducted studies with the intention of identifying information needs of farmers. Lionberger and Chang(1970), Benor and Boxter(1984), Wilkening (1950), Hasker (1971) are some of the works at international level where farmers' information needs have been analyzed. At the national level Goel et al (1998), Gaikwad et. al. (1972), Rao (1991), Tiwari et al (1997), Dave et al (1978), Thombre et. el. (1986), Aher (1999) have all studied various aspects of information needs of farmers. Most of these workers have concentrated on relation of the information need to various socio economic aspects. Few of them like Dikle (1990) have also dealt with information quality aspects like reliability and credibility. Comparison of various Terminal sources like radio, television have also been subjects of study.

The current mechanism of taking information from its point of origin to the farm where the actual application takes place involves designated extension workers prominently. Information needs of these workers themselves have been area of interest of Hunter (1970), Akhouri (1973), and Pandey (1979).

The very impact of the Training and Visit system of carrying information to farmers was evaluated by Vedpathak (1997), Ghuge (1984), Sorekar (1989). Shinde and Abdul (2000) have studied the problem of information needs of research workers in the area of agriculture, whereas Digraskar (1996) has tried to tackle problems of farmer, extension works and research workers simultaneously with regard to information needs.

There have been hardly any studies where information needs of marketiers, financiers and businessmen have been dealt with. However many studies of market studies of regulated agricultural markets are available (Dalvi (1992), Pokle (1994), Chandel (1980), Mogal (1989).

Use of Geographical Information Systems in agriculture is one area where lot of work is reported. Maji and Krishna (1996), Maji et al (1998), Venkataratnam(2001) and Obi Reddy et al (2001) are few instances of these. Though techniques of crop acreage estimation, soil resource identification etc are developed they are not readily available on any information network for ready use of farmers and planners.

There are instances of connecting farmers, extension workers, and researchers through networked community teleservices. Rosaiah and Palanisamy (2001) have presented a good account of Panela Net of Columbia, Farming and Rural Expertise and Dissemination Services of Greece, Warna Wired Vilage Project of Maharashtra and Information Villages Project of Swaminathan Research Foundation.

1.2 Websites and Portals

Few websites and portals run by State Agriculture Universities with assistance from National Informatics Centre, a few run by organizations like Fertilizer Corporation of India, Indian Council of Agricultural Research and affiliated institutes are available.

Few of these are reviewed here.

http://raitamitra.kar.nic.in, this website provides information regarding the Information and tips to farmers, weekly weather report and crop area information, farm mechanization, crop condition, seed position, fertilizer position and market prices.

http://www.exportersindia.net/fertilizers.htm provides addresses of fertilizer buyers, fertilizers manufacturers, fertilizers suppliers, fertilizers exporters, fertilizers importers, fertilizers products, fertilizers trade leads, farm - input fertilizers, pesticides and seeds from all countries.

http://www.icar.org.in gives information about research activities and institutes, crop science, animal science, horticulture, fisheries, agricultural engineering, education and extension.

These websites or portals require more state (or region) specific information content.

1.3 Objectives of the current study

Literature survey and survey of current portals clearly indicated that more serious probe into problems of agricultural information systems is necessary to clarify many aspects. The problems are so complex that it may not be possible in any single study to examine all of them. Hence we have set up objectives for the current study with limited but specific goals in mind.

The specific objectives set for the study were:

1. To probe into the current scenario of information availability to farmers, planners, research workers.
2. To define the concept of 'Agro Information System', and

propose different models to suit various requirements.

3. To conduct a system analysis exercise to identify data flow mechanisms, information generating agencies and their linkages.
4. To patemeterize the various subsystems of the 'Agro Information System', in terms of their scope, information content design, tools to be used and target users.

1.4 Organization of the Chapters

With the above aspects in view the current study has been carried out. The work is presented in eight chapters.

The first chapter, which is the current chapter, is devoted to the general introduction to the subject matter.

The second chapter is devoted to problem identification where the need for an Agro Information System is emphasized. Inadequacies of the current arrangements of information dissemination have been identified. Attempt has been made to project Computer Network-based and IT enabled information systems as possible efficient alternatives.

Chapter three contains details of System Analysis conducted. Specifically logistics, data flow diagrams, data dictionary have been provided with respect to subsystems like Agricultural marketing, Irrigation. System analysis of Research and education has also been presented. In respect of extension, which is the base of traditional information system, the training and visit system of state department of agriculture is presented. Traditionally agricultural extension has been synonymous to farm information dissemination, hence it defines the current status.

Chapter four is devoted for discussion on design of an Information system. Criteria for selection of hardware, communication media have been initially presented and then detailed discussion on application software to meet specific needs is given. Exclusive section on special tools is incorporated, where details of search engines, statistical tools, simulators and Geographic Information System tools are discussed.

Chapter fifth, sixth, seventh and eight are devoted to specific subsystems like farm-advisory, Agricultural Marketing, irrigation, research and education. Though these four systems do not cover the whole of the Agro Information System, these have been presented here because they are singularly important.

In chapter five a search mechanism presented forms one of the special attributes of farm-advisory system. A mechanism has been set up for query posting and expert response. Meteorological information and weather forecasting is also treated as a part of farm advisory system.

In chapter six Agricultural marketing systems has been viewed as a Neural network system and has been analyzed.

Online administrative processing of forms, irrigation-request forms from users, is one of the techniques that is illustrated in chapter seven.

Agricultural education is almost synonymous with rural education and the quality and level of agricultural education determines ultimately quality of agricultural production. How to get education and where to get education could be questions asked by a farm information seeker. Hence this is one of the most important information systems included in chapter eight.

The Analysis and Information presented in this book should be useful to network based online information system designers, planners and administrators taking care of farm activities alike.

Chapter 2
Problem Identification

2.0 Introduction

In this chapter a few fundamental issues are addressed to. As a consequence of these discussions the questions like 'is there a need for a computer network based information system ?' and 'whether such an information system can really do better than the existing systems which are responsible for information dissemination?' will be answered to a large extent. Full satisfaction of information need possibly can never be achieved. With better technology only one can reduce the gap between the need and the supply. Many research workers have surveyed the current information network and have identified the shortfalls in the current setup. We will be using their results in our analysis.

2.1 Need and perpetuality:

We begin with the hypothesis.

Hypothesis 1: *Farmers, Agro-processors, Marketiers, Extension workers, Financiers, Research workers, Administrators, Students are all in perpetual need of information regarding agriculture and related aspects.*

In support of the above hypothesis many evidences are presented. Table 2.1 shows that a farmer seeks information on different aspects of package of practices. The Table 2.2 shows that a farmer tries to access information from different sources with varied degrees of intensity (Thombre (1979), Novak and Stegelin(1988)). Results in Table 2.1 and 2.2 though are results of a survey conducted around 1978, are still indicative of the fact that the farmer is in search of information and he tries to access various sources. A survey by Rao (1991) shows that the programme "Amachi mati aamachi manas" is equally popular as the 'news' on Doordarshan, with a viewership of above 95% among the farmers, whereas all other programmes including entertainment programmes have viewership below 50%. There are ample studies on effectiveness of special Radio telecasts and Television broadcasts, for farmers conducted on a period of past twenty years (Satpute (1985), Mane (1988), Patil (2000), Bhosle (2000), Aher (1999), Kubde and Choudhary (1992) are few examples. All these works provide ample evidence to the fact that farmers need information, and the need is perpetual.

Table 2.1: Information received by farmers through mass media:

Sr. No.	Information on	Percentage*
1	Improved seed	72.67
2	Improved cultivation methods	66.00
3	Proper and efficient use of fertilizer	70.67
4	*Plant protection measures*	
	a) Insecticides	88.00
	b) Fungicides	39.33
	c) Weedicides	8.00
5	Improved farm implements	22.67
6	Other aspects like marketing, dairy and poultry farming	21.33

Source: Thombre (1979).

* Percentage of farmers receiving information.

Table 2.2:

a) Sources of farm information and measures of their differential use: Regional rankings

Sr. No	*Sources of information*	*Percentage farmer who access*				*Rank*
		Always	Sometimes	Rarely	Never	
1	Radio	44.7	49.3	--	6.00	I
2	Farm literature	34.7	40.7	9.3	15.3	II
3	Film shows	0.0	32.0	46.0	22.0	III
4	Exhibition	0.0	20.7	63.3	16.0	IV

Source: Thombre (1979).

b) Sources of farm information: International rankings (a 14-state survey in U.S. –1984)	
Sources of information	*Rank*
Magazine / newspaper	1
Extension service	2
Friends, neighbors, relatives	3
Seminars and workshops other than extension	4
School, college courses	5
Miscellaneous	6
Children's interest	7
T.V. advertising	8
Competitors	9
Radio	10
Source: Novak and Stegelin (1988).	

Study of Digraskar (1996), provides evidence to the fact that not only farmers but extension workers and researchers also need information. Suryawanshi (1992) has observed that extension workers do need training in different areas (Table 2.3). Hunter (1970) observed that Agricultural universities in India communicate with Extension workers through publications, radio talks, farmer fair and exhibition, it means that the information generated from researcher will be disseminated by Extension worker to a farmer. Pokale (1994) have studied Agricultural Produce Market Committee (APMC) of Parbhani. It is evident from study that Databases on arrivals, prices are regularly maintained by these committees. Making this information available to farmers on an efficient network could be beneficial.

Table 2.3: Extent of needs of training of T&V worker:

(Estimated percentage of T&V workers who need training.)

A) Aspect: Crop information				
Sr. No		High	Medium	Low
1.	Kharif Jawar	72.50	27.50	0.0
2.	Tur	5.00	41.25	53.75
3.	Mung	5.00	40.00	55.00
4.	Kharif groundnut	23.75	7.50	8.75

Sr. No		High	Medium	Low
5.	Summer groundnut	12.50	43.75	43.75
6.	Sunflower	28.75	66.25	5.00
7.	Cotton	72.50	27.50	0.0
8.	Horticulture crops	52.50	31.25	16.25
9.	Vegetables	25.00	37.50	37.50
10.	Rabi Jawar	50.00	43.75	6.25
11.	Safflower	0.0	25.00	75.00
B) Aspect: Crop cultivation practices				
1.	Preparatory tillage	0.0	40.00	60.00
2.	Application of manures	6.25	31.25	62.50
3.	Sowing	10.00	15.00	75.00
4.	Irrigation management	28.75	46.25	25.00
5.	Application of fertilizers	77.50	22.50	0.0
6.	Plant protection measures	73.75	26.25	0.0
7.	Intercultural operations	10.00	47.50	42.50
8.	Improved farm machinery	41.25	58.75	0.0
9.	Seed programme	35.00	65.00	0.0
10.	Soil testing	50.00	40.00	10.00
C) Aspect: Methods of extension				
1.	Giving information effectively to farmers	68.75	31.25	0.0
2.	Arranging demonstration	53.75	46.25	0.0
3.	Conducting farmers meeting	26.25	73.75	0.0
4.	Organizing krishi melawa	21.25	78.75	0.0
5.	Arranging field visits	30.00	63.75	6.25
6.	Organizing field day	0.0	22.50	77.50
7.	Effective use of Radio / TV	10.00	81.25	8.75
8.	Effective use of Agril. Periodicals & booklets	0.0	82.50	17.50
9.	Running shetkari mandal	0.0	3.25	68.75

Source: Adapted from Suryawanshi (1992)

The need of information is perpetual because at any point of time there is always a knowledge gap between current technology and the technology used by the farmers. Table 2.4 gives estimates measures of such a gap in two different crops. This is only indicative of the fact that with advancement of technology there is always a gap in knowledge which requires to be filled.

Table 2.4: Measures of Gap in knowledge: (in percentage)

Sr. No	Knowledge on	Percentage of farmers with knowledge gap.	
		Rabi Jawar	Cotton
1	Seed rate required per hectare	14.17	22.5
2	Period required for harvesting	18.34	20.00
3	Correct spacing between two lines	38.34	30.00
4	Fertilizer use per hectare	41.67	40.84
5	Control of pests	57.5	50.84
6	Number of irrigations required	48.34	43.34
7	Waterstress bearing capacity of improved variety	45.84	--
8	Sulphur treatment to seed before sowing	66.67	--
9	Factors responsible for heavy infestation of disease	58.34	--
10	Suitable soil type	66.67	--
11	Control of weed	62.5	53.34
12	Yield of improved varieties	40.84	24.17
13	Reusing of seeds for next year	41.67	42.5

Source: Adapted from Vedapathak (1997).

Thus we have established that hypothesis 1 is reasonably true.

2.2 Sources and attributes of existing information system

Next we examine the nature of existing information systems

and their attributes. Universities, agricultural departments of the government have been providing information on agriculture for years together under Benor scheme and lately through T&V systems, we now hypothesize:

Hypothesis 2: *The existing information system relies mainly on three channels of information dissemination, namely*

A) *Radio and Television,*

B) *Print media,*

C) *Personal contact and their major attributes are credibility, faith and reachability.*

Major advantages and disadvantages of these channels are mentioned in Table 2.5. As we progress, in subsequent chapter we will try and prove that with modern IT tools it is possible to build an information system which has better attributes than the current systems. These channels have been ranked differently by farmers mainly according to their credibility, reachability and faith. It is evident from the Tables 2.6 and 2.7 that Doordarshan seems to have better credibility and better faith compared to Radio which has got a moderate credibility and faith. However in case of overall effectiveness Radio and Doordarshan both are at par. However both these electronic media have the disadvantage of being channels of unidirectional flow of information. Among the electronic and other sources farmer seem to have better linking of personal contact as indicated by ranking Table 2.8. This must be because the personal contacts have an advantage of bi-directional exchange of information. In a bi-directional exchange queries and doubts are cleared then and there.

Table 2.5: Major advantages and disadvantages of different channels:

Channel	Advantages	Disadvantages
Radio and Television	Reachability	Unidirectional
Print media	---	Unidirectional and low reachability
Personal contact	Bi-directional	Low reachability

Table 2.6: Evaluation of Doordarshan by farmers as a source of information

Level	(Percentage of farmers)			
	Credibility	Reliability (faith)	Actual viewing	Overall effectiveness
High	56.67	54.00	15.33	18.00
Medium	32.67	40.67	74.00	68.00
Low	10.66	5.33	10.67	14.00

Source: Adapted from Patil (2000).

Table 2.7: Evaluation of Radio as a source of information by farmers

Level	(Percentage of farmers)			
	Credibility	Reliability (faith)	Actual listening	Overall effectiveness
High	10.67	31.33	10.66	15.33
Medium	82.00	57.34	70.00	68.67
Low	07.33	11.33	19.33	16.00

Source: Adapted from Bhosle (2000).

Table 2.8: Relative credibility different sources of information perceived by farmers

Sr. No.	Information source	Rank	Rank
1	Extension worker	I	--
2	Radio	IV	II
3	Television	--	I
4	Demonstration	II	--
5	Friends	V	--
6	Agricultural literature	III	III, IV
7	Film shows	--	V
Source :- Adapted from		Satpute (1985)	Rao (1991)

Bellurkar (1990) has conducted a study in view to obtain distribution of the televiewers according to their mass media exposure, frequency of viewing farm and home telecast and also credibility of television. Sandhu (1973) observed that radio was rated higher in source credibility than the block official, progressive farmers, leaflets and newspaper. Satpute. (1985) has indicated that extension worker is perceived as a most credible source by the big and small farmers, while demonstration was ranked as most credible source by the medium farmers. Agricultural literature and radio were ranked second and third in order of sequence as most credible sources by the big and small farmers. Further, extension workers, agricultural literature and friends were some other credible sources used in descending order. Goyal et. al. (1998) have observed that considerable percentage of television viewers are women, their needs are different from male viewers. Farmers have also opined that duration of broadcasting and telecasting should be extended, it means that need of viewers are still not satisfied (Saxena et. al. (1995)). We may draw inference from these facts that need of credible but at the same time bi-directional information system still exists. The channels as identified in the hypothesis have varied levels of credibility, faith and reliability.

2.3 Inadequacy of current information system:

Next thing to examine is the adequacy of the existing systems. In this respect we hypothesize:

Hypothesis 3: *The existing information system is inadequate mainly because of the following shortfalls:*

A) *Noise:* The distortion of information from the point of its origin before it reaches the destination.

B) *Uni-directionality:* Currently most information transfer techniques involve unidirectional broadcast of information without provision for adequate feedback and bi-directional interaction.

C) *Delayed response:* In some cases where user has provision to query the system, the replies are not immediate and there is a large time gap between the initiation of the query and receipt of the response.

D) *Problem of language:* Many farmers feel the language used for telecasting and broadcasting are generally not suitable for rural viewers and listeners.

Now we discuss each of the above shortfalls one by one.

Noise: The information does not reach to the user in its original and correct form. The evidence for existence of noise comes from the fact that credibility and faith of different channels of information dissemination vary. More is the noise less is the faith of the client system.

Uni-directionality: Lionberger and Chang (1970) found that researcher requires feedback from the farmer in order to generate new information by using existing information or self observation. Researcher needed information at any time but at the same time feedback is not possible with existing communication channel so there is highly need of bi-directional mode of communication. Digraskar (1996) found that farmer, extension worker and researcher needs information but they are inter-dependent to each other. They need a communication facility that connected to each other. Hence bi-directionality is a very important attribute.

Delayed response: Extension worker provides information to the farmer and if any kind of difficulty is not solved by extension worker then he replies later to the farmer after confirmation but time goes off. So delay arises in communication.

Problem of language: Many workers have observed that there are problems regarding the language used in broadcasts. Aher (1999) found that 13.00 per cent of the respondents wanted 'technical' terms should be simplified into regional language. Kubde and Choudhari (1992), reveal that 72.38 per cent farmers suggested 'to use local language', while 43.00 per cent farmers wanted to 'avoid the use of technical words'. Mane (1988) observed that 89.33 per cent televiewers understood language completely and 10.67 per cent televiewers understood partially. There are two aspects to this problem. First is to use local language. Second is to convert technical terms into common terms.

2.4 Information Technology (IT) based information system as possible solution:

We have seen so far that the existing information channels have many attributes which require improvements. With this fact in view we hypothesize:

Hypothesis 4: *A Computer Network based and IT enabled information system with the following attributes*

- *Large credibility,*
- *Full faith of users,*
- *Which will not transmit noise,*
- *Which provides for bi-directional communication and where time lag between query and response is minimal,*
- *It is based on local language with simplified technical terms for understanding of a common man, and*
- *which will reach every user effectively,* can be established.

Extension experts Prakash and Venkatramani (2000) have stressed the need for setting up "Information kiosks" with computer networks as possible future extension agency for effective training of farmers, dissemination of information etc. A natural connectivity of this network to an agricultural marketing information system will facilitate an efficient functioning of the agriculture business and will definitely benefit the farmer who is the principle producer of agricultural goods, in choosing appropriate markets, appropriate products. A survey conducted in U. S. (Novak and Stegelin, 1988) indicates that farmers are waiting for more and better information on computers. They generally state non-availability of proper software as the reasons for not using computers. One of the plus points is that farmer do not feel intimidated by micro computers. The findings are decade old no doubt, but the fact remains that the study showed that farmers are more concerned about information and software rather than being intimidated about the computers.

From the above discussion, it is very much clear that, the computer-based network would have advantages than other sources of information. The advantage of Radio and Television is that, they are based on broadband technology but flow of information is unidirectional. Problems regarding language, bi-directionality of exchanges, time loss in communication are solvable. Computer communication network is not based on broadband technology, this could be a disadvantage when we compare internet with television and radio. In the near future, internet will be definitely based on Broadband technology which will take care of this problem (http://www.artsact.com/technical.htm).

Chapter 3
System Analysis

3.0 Introduction

Agriculture is inextricably interwoven with progress of civilization. It is a source of perpetual creation on which civilization depends. Creation of information and exchange of information musthave been taking place all along the evolution of Agriculture itself. In fact in case of early stages of civilization, evolution of agriculture was almost synonymous to evolution of civilization itself. A virtual information system has been in existence in the society essentially self-evolved, self-managed with no one in particular but the society itself as the underlying supporting layer. Information systems are omnipresent. It is only the architecture and tools which have changed over the time period. In this chapter we will try to present results of a methodical study of the virtual Agro Information System as it currently exits. To begin with we hypothesize

> *A Virtual Agro Information System (VAIS) is in existence, it is a self evolved system, with no particular ownership or an organized agency to run, which is capable of manipulating, updating, analyzing, storing, capturing data relevant to all aspects of Agricultural production, marketing, financing, Agro based industrial activities, Agricultural education, geographically referenced information on soil classification, meteorological information, and is helpful for problem solving, decision-making and running advisory services for agricultural planners, research workers, farmers, extension workers, education seekers and businessmen alike.*

Existence of such a system can always be experienced but can never be proved. Hence we have hypothesized the concept.

3.1 System Analysis: Methodology

Once existence of such a system is accepted we can proceed with a systematic analysis of it using the standard tools (Awad,

1998) of system analysis.

The following is the list of some of the tools used in the analysis.

Basic Definitions of System Components

System Charts

Relational diagrams

Data Bases

Data Dictionaries

Data flow diagram (DFD),

Data processing tools to generate information,

Decision tree,

Decision tables, Pros and Cons of each tool.,

Organizational Charts,

Logistics,

Information generation methods,

Information flow diagrams,

Network diagrams and

Hierarchical structures.

System analysis that would parameterize the needs of farmers, planners and research workers is our main objective which we would like to achieve as a part of system analysis. In this chapter we look in the problem of Agro info system as a whole. Some micro level parameterization specific to some of the subsystems will be discussed in Ch 5 to 8 where individual components are dealt with.

3.1.1 The Survey

An extensive survey, by personal interview method was conducted for the purpose of systems analysis. Table 3.1 gives details of the distribution of experts and informants contacted.

Table 3.1: Distribution of the Informants for the System analysis

Department/Institution	Post	Number
State Department of Agriculture	Sub Divisional Agril.	1
	Taluka Agril. Officer	1
	Mandal Agril. Oficer	2
	Agril. Supervisor	5
	Agril. Assistant	8
Marathwada Agricultural University	Professor	2
	Associate Professor	12
	Assistant Professor	8
Agricultural Produce Marketing Committees	Asstt. Secretary	1
	Trader	5
	Commission agent	5
	Farmer	15
State Department of Irrigation	Section Engineer (S.E.)	2
	Canal Inspector	3
	Sr. Clerk	3
	Clerk	5

3.1.2 The Secondary Data:

Sources of secondary information like district statistical abstracts, annual reports of All India Radio, Doordarshan, reports of extension studies were referred to in many cases, to supplement the information gathered by interviews.

An extensive survey of Portals and Websites related to agriculture was done with the help of search engines on the Internet. A list of sites visited is given in Table 3.7.

3.2 Targeted geographic area and targeted users:

Our targeted area is Marathwada region (Map 3), consisting of seven districts viz. Aurangabad, Jalna, Beed, Latur, Osmanabad, Nanded and Parbhani. Geographically the region is situated between $17^0 36'$ N $20^0 40'$ N Latitude and $74^0 40'$ E and $78^0 15'$ E longitude. The total Geographical area of the region is 64,525 Sq. kilometers, which is 12 per cent of Maharashtra. The population of the region according to 1991 census was 127.79 lac which formed about 16.23 per cent of the state (Kasle,1998). Table 3.2 shows population distribution of Marathwada region

Table 3.2: Population distribution of Marathwada region by profession:

District	No. of talukas	Profession				Total population
		Farming	Agril. Labour	Livestock, forestry, fishing, hunting, orchards & allied activities	Transports & storage communication	
Aurangabad	8	3,65,178	2,51,297	11,018	20,302	22,13,779
Jalna	8	2,80,492	2,13,787	7,274	7,572	13,64,425
Parbhani	12	3,46,818	3,68,736	11,503	12,952	21,17,035
Beed	9	3,72,658	2,31,452	12,833	11,691	18,22,072
Nanded	9	3,40,709	3,83,205	11,571	14,123	23,30,374
Osmanabad	6	2,14,496	2,17,527	6,069	7,054	12,76,327
Latur	7	2,58,428	2,56,672	5,057	10,114	16,76,641
Total	59	21,78,779	19,22,676	65,325	83,808	1,28,00653

Source: Statistical abstract of M.S.(2000).

by profession. It is evident from the figures that around 42 lac people are almost directly connected to agricultural profession.

Targeted users for the information system are the farmers, research workers, extension workers engaged in agricultural research, T&V officials, and staff of the directorate of extension, Marathwada Krishi Vidyapeeth, staff engaged in teaching agriculture at colleges and schools, marketers, financiers and workers in seed industries, other agro-processing industries, the irrigation equipment, producers and dealers.

Table 3.3: T&V workers, research worker and students of agricultural schools and colleges:

a) Logistics of T&V department in Parbhani district (including Hingoli district.):	
Designation	*Number*
District superintendent officer	1
Deputy director of agriculture	1
Sub-divisional agricultural officer	2
Seed testing officer	1
Technical officer	10
Taluka agricultural officer	12
Soil survey officer	1
Agricultural officer	60
Agricultural supervisor	137
Agricultural assistant	484
Source: T&V department, Parbhani	
b) Logistics of research worker in Marathwada region:	
Designation	*Number*
Professor and above	053
Associate professor	165
Assistant professor	262
	Total = 480
c) Logistics of agricultural student in Marathwada region:	
Category	*Number of students*
Undergraduate degree course	0528
Post graduate degree course	0140
Ph.D. degree course	0029
Agricultural school	3060
	Total = 3757

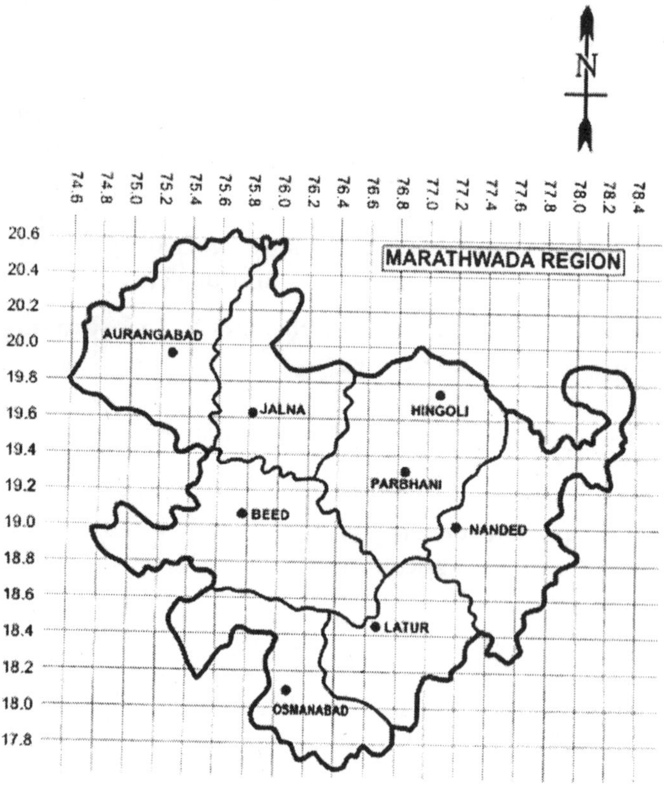

Map 3 : Marathwada Region - Targeted area

Table 3.3 shows logistics of T&V workers, research workers and students of agricultural schools and colleges. It is very difficult to estimate exact targeted population which will be interested in agricultural information. However, it is clear from Tables 3.2 and 3.3 that nearly 42 lac farm workers and few thousand extension workers, research workers and students will be interested in agricultural information. Hence this number must form the core target. Hence we have

A total of 43 lac individuals distributed over an area of 64,525 sq kms of area of Marathwada region are the potential target population for the Agro information system. They will surely find use of the system with varying intensity and frequency.

Having identified the target area and target population, now we proceed to analyze the currently used channels through which information is carried to the end users of information.

3.3 Modes of dissemination of Information

Our study revealed that in general there are three modes of dissemination of information that were effectively engaged in disseminating the information. This fact was hypothesized in Ch 2, Hypothesis 2. They were

Electronic media

Direct communications

Print media

Electronic media constitutedof radio broadcasts, television programmes and the internet. Direct communications constituted of visits of extension workers, farmer rallies, exhibitions, extension workshops, advisory services from subject matter specialists and so on. Print media constituted of extension publications, newspaper articles, periodicals, booklets and so on.

3.3.1 Electronic media:

3.3.1.1 Radio:

The All India Radio (AIR) is the only agency providing radio transmission services in the Marathwada Region. Currently no national channel broadcast is located in the Marathwada region. There are two regional radio stations, one at Aurangabad with 1kw MW strength and one at 20 kw MW is situated at Parbhani. Put together they cover the population of 105.4 lakh which is 82.33% of the total population of the region. Local radio stations at Beed, Nanded and Osmanabad of 6 kw strength with FM band cover an additional population of 36.9 lakhs. Geographically the total coverage is approximately around area of 250 km radius. Local and Regional radio stations provide Agricultural information, News, Music and other programmes. Table 3.4 and Map 1 show locations of radio stations and their coverage. Table 3.5 shows list of Agricultural programme on radio:

Table 3.4: Locations of Radio stations and Their coverage in Marathwada

No.	Place	Date of commission-ing	Transmission strength	Station type	Population covered in lakhs
1.	Aurangabad	19-09-1976	1 kw MW (10-12 km coverage)	Regional	17.4
2.	Parbhani	16-03-1998	20 kw MW (250 km coverage)	Regional	88
3.	Beed	10-11-1990	6 kw FM (LRS) (60 km coverage)	Local	11
4.	Nanded	29-05-1991	6 kw FM (LRS) (60 km coverage)	Local	14.9
5.	Osmanabad	09-12-1996	6 kw FM (LRS) (60 km coverage)	Local	11

Source: Chambhargekar (2001)

Table 3.5: List of Agricultural programmes on radio:

Serial no.	Name of programme
1	Shetkaryansathi
2	Hawaman andaaz
3	Gaonkaryansathi
4	Kamgar jagat
5	Aamacha ghar aamacha shiwar
6	Nabhowani shetkari
7	Lok jagar

3.3.1.2 Doordarshan:

Map 2 shows location of television stations and their coverage over Marathwada. A 100watt power of transmitting station covers 30 km radial distance and 10 kw power covers 80 km radial distance.

The effective radius depends on radiation source power (satellite) and height of the radiating antenna of the transmitting station. Doordarshan and Sahyadri are (viewed differently) due to change in the frequency and tuning it time to time as per schedule.

From Map 2 it is clear that nearly Doordarshan covers the whole of the geographic area of Marathwada region.

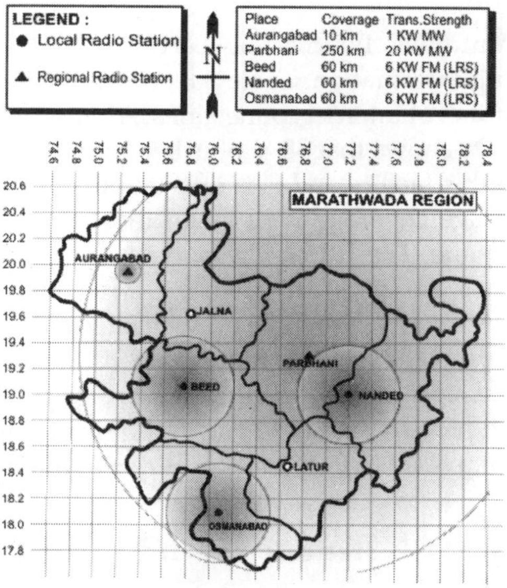

Map 1 : Location of Radio stations and their coverage.

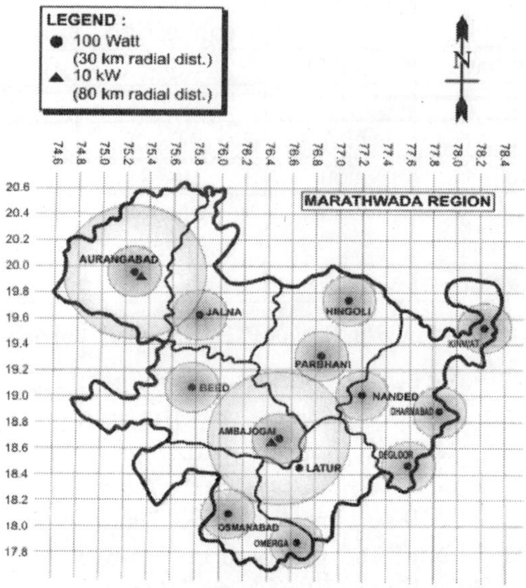

Map 2 : Location of Doordarshan stations and their coverage.

3.3.1.3 Internet:

In recent days, Internet has become a very effective tool for acquiring information. Table 3.6 shows BSNL stations and allotted number of internet connections. A conservative estimate of reachability shows that 38 % of urban population is currently covered by this facility and 8 % of total population is covered. The percentage coverage is so small that current coverage is very inadequate. The list of few portals and web sites related to agriculture are given in Table 3.7. Most of the static and dynamic information available on web sites are not specific to Marathwada. They give information on national and international level. Information related to cropping pattern, soil type, climatic condition, market news, on-line forms processing tools etc not available in the site and this is the major need of our region.

Table 3.6: BSNL stations and its allotted number of connections

BSNL station name	Dial-up	Leased line	VSAT
Parbhani	850	No connection	2
Aurangabad	10000	9	10
Beed	6	N.A.	N.A.
Jalna	N.A.	N.A.	N.A.
Latur	550	10-12	No connection
Nanded	950	No connection	2-3
Osmanabad	N.A.	N.A.	N.A.

Source: Oral discussion with P.A. of Parbhani BSNL department

A novel concept of connecting villages with a computer based communication network, is being tried at Warnanagar, an hours drive from Kolhapur ((http://members.tripod.com/~TKIET_SHIT_Group/) . It is a part of farmer's co-opertaive movement. With 10 servers, two V-SAT's (very small aperture terminals)and about 165 personal computers and an Internet Kiosk in every village (70 of 'em) Warana is the first rural networking projectin India catering to 400,000 . No such project

Table 3.7: Farm related web sites:

Name of Web site or source	Membership necessity (Y / N)	Services provided or available information	Remark
www.agriculture.com	Yes	Markets, news, weather, magazine, radio, subscribe, customer service, commodity price updation etc.	Online market prices and magazine facility required.
www.accuspray.com	No	Pipe fittings, tanks, pumps, spray controls, spray guns, strainers, valves.	Equipment name with technical details required.
www.fertindia.com	No	Fertilizer agencies, availability, transportation.	Network of seed and fertilizer agecies required.
www.fadinap.org	--	--	URL not found
www.uttamkrishi.com	No	General information on agriculture.	Bi-directional communication required.
www.foodtrader.com			
www.raitamitra.kar.nic.in	NA	Crop condition, seed & fertilizer position, crop area, market prices, yearly figures of yield, production, productivity, tips to farmer.	As per soil type, which crop to grow and when to grow.

Name of Web site or source	Membership necessity (Y / N)	Services provided or available information	Remark
www.agriwatch.com	Yes	Research reports, market watch & prices, agril. News watch, general news, buy & sell bulletin.	Dynamic interaction is required.
www.agmachine-india.com	--	--	URL not found
www.agroservice.hu	No	Agmachine publication, on-line magazines, global agril. Machinery, world agril. Equipment, market reports.	Not suitable for Marathwada region.
www.undp.org	No	Agril. Software, e-commerce & agriculture, market prices, networking & newsletter, farm shows, list of agril. Co-operatives FAO agril. Marketing etc.	Information related to loan facility details required.
www.engfarmchina.com	NA	Industry channels, agmachinery, food & processing, fertilizer, planting seeds, organic products, grain & oil.	Machinery installation procedure required.

Name of Web site or source	Membership necessity (Y / N)	Services provided or available information	Remark
www.indiaagronet.com	No	Agri-News, Market Update, Agri. Resources, Ag.-Technologies, Agri-Knowledge, Agri-Services, Agri-Organization, Agri-Companies , Agri-Communities, Feedback Events (New), Tips for Farmers , Advertisement opportunities.	Online services required
www.farmers.com	No	Details of insurance policy.	As per farmer category, insurance details required.
www.powerfarm.com	--	--	URL not found
www.indianagriculture.com	--	--	URL not found
www.industrialtradefair.com	--	--	URL not found

Name of Web site or source	Membership necessity (Y / N)	Services provided or available information	Remark
www.agriintex.com	No	AGRI INTEX 2002 is a mega Agri International Fair of India organized by CODISSIA with the support of Government of India, State Governments, Universities, Research and Academic Institutions, Development Agencies and Corporations in Agricultural sectors. Information of Agril. International Exhibition.	Online information facility required.
www.khetibadi.com	--	--	URL not found
www.ekrishimitra.com	No	Rates, brokers, transport, auction, govt. scheme, export.	Mechanism must consist every district of M.S.
www.kisan.com	Yes	Farm land – buy / sell / lease, organic farming, medical & aromatic plants, campus agril. Education, agril. Produce, equipment & machinery, world farm prices, wholesale prices of commercial & non – commercial crops.	As per need of farmer, contents specification is needed.

seems to have been undertaken in Marathwada.

One more case of mass based information system which uses computer network has been established at Dhar district of Madha Pradesh(Rajora R and Vyas N, 2001). Computers in 21 major centers in five blocks of the district were connected through an intranet network named Gyandoot ("purveyor of knowledge"). Local rural youth acted as entrepreneurs for running cyber cafes - cum - cyber offices on low cost commercial lines without salary or stipend. These were called Soochanalayas ("Information centres"). Soochanalayas available to provide needs of government departments and panchayats (local governing councils) were met free of cost. Some of the services on the Intranet have been integrated with the Internet (www.gyandoot.net).

3.3.2 Direct communication

By Direct communication, we mean only face-to-face communication between individuals and personally delivered letters, documents etc. One system using direct communication is the "Training and Visit System" of agricultural extension, evolved by Danial Benor. The direct communication takes place between VEW and farmer.

Agricultural Technology Information Centre (ATIC):

Keeping in view the need of the farmers, the Marathwada Agricultural University has very recently started a ATIC. The following services are expected to be provided:

a) Sale of Technological products,
b) Technical Guidance,
c) Diagnosis of crop disorders,
d) Information services through Internet, Telephone (02452-29000) and advisory,
e) Training to students and extension functionaries

Such an information provides an opportunity for users to directly access aspects from university. Since ATIC is expected to be equipped with Short Messaging services (SMS). This centre will have an important role to play in the near future.

3.3.3 Print media

By Print media, we mean the commonly referred media like newspapers, books, magazines like Shetkari, Sheti-Bhati, Baliraja etc.

Table 3.8 shows estimated distribution of the farmers who use farm journals like Sheti-Bhati and Shetakari and circulation statistics of commonly used Lokmat newspaper. In Table 3.9 measure of effectiveness of knowledge gain after reading agricultural information from newspapers, is reported.

Table 3.8: Estimated distribution of the farmers who use farm journals and popular newspapers statistics

Place	Farm journals		Lokmat paper circulation
	Sheti-Bhati	Shetkari	
Aurangabad	97,393	65,732	30000
Jalna	74,807	50,489	14000
Parbhani	92,496	62,427	13000
Beed	99,388	67,079	14000
Nanded	90,867	61,328	25000
Osmanabad	57,206	38,610	13000
Latur	68,923	46,517	20000
Total	5,81,080	3,92,182	129000
Source:	Adapted from Thombre (1979).		Dikle (1990).

Source: Adapted from Thombre (1979). Dikle (1990).

Table 3.9: Measure of effectiveness of knowledge gained after reading agricultural information from newspapers

Sr. No.	Category	Percentage
1.	Got additional knowledge about agriculture	90.00
2.	Developed interest about implementation of new agricultural technology	64.70
3.	Favorable attitude for new agricultural technology developed	70.00
4.	Acquired skill by the practice due to new information of Agriculture	38.00
5.	Motivated to put into practice new agricultural technology	58.00

Source: Sonawane (2000).

3.4 Information Generation /Production Mechanisms and agencies.

3.4.1 Information for Farming

There are four major warehouses of information on which a practicing farmer depends.

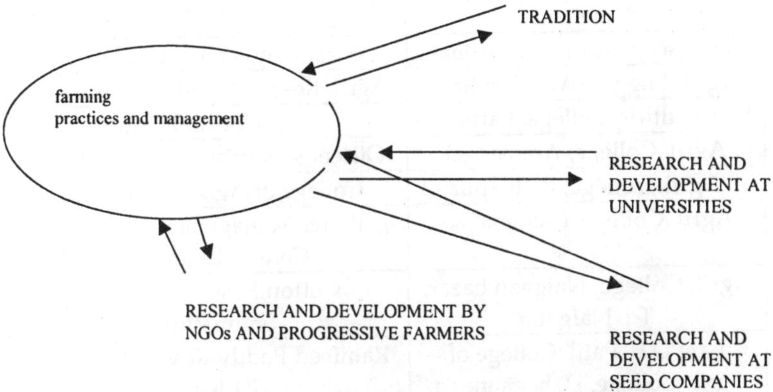

Tradition is an ever evolving warehouse. Its contents simply keep increasing. What is modern technology today becomes an established common technology after some time and ultimately it gets merged into traditional information base.

In other words information initially new, transforms into common and later transforms into traditional knowledge and simply shifts itself from warehouse to warehouse.

The state supports research and developmentthrough four agricultural universities in the state out of which one is situated in the region of Marathwada.

A list of research stations exclusively devoted for specific information generation is given in Table 3.10. Similarly a list of seed companies (prominent only) and active NGOs is given in tables 3.11 and 3.12 respectively.

Table 3.10: List of Agricultural colleges and Research stations in Marathwada region

Agricultural college	Research station
Agril. College, Parbhani	Agril. School, Aurangabad.
Agril. College, Latur	National Agril. Research project, A'bad
Food Technology College, Parbhani	Fruit research station, A'bad
Home science, MAU, Parbhani	Krishi vigyan kendra, A'bad
Agril. Engg. MAU, Parbhani	Agril. Research Station, Badnapur
Horticulture College, Parbhani	Agril. School, Latur
Agril. College, Ambajogai	Oilseeds rResearch Station, Latur
Agril. College, Badnapur	College of Agriculture, Latur
Agril. College, Osmanabad	Water Management Research Centre, Khamgaon
Agril. College, Naigaon bazar, Tq. Naigaon	Cotton Research Station, Somnathpur
Late D.P. Patil, College of Agril. College, Dahegaon, Tq. Vaijapur	Rainfeed Paddy Research Station, Tuljapur
Late R.G. College of Agril. Jintur road, Parbhani	Oilseeds Research sub-campus, Ambejogai
Aditya Agril. College, Kala Hanuman Thana, Beed	Agril. School, Ambejogai
Horticulture College, Georai Tanda, Aurangabad	Taluka Seed Farm, Ambejogai
--	Experiment on Cultivators (E.C.F.), Ambejogai
--	Cotton Research Station, Nanded
--	Agril School, Nanded
--	Regional Sugarcane Research Station, Basmat
--	College of Agril., Osmanabad
--	College of Agril. Badnapur
--	College of Agril. Ambejogai
--	Bajara research station, Vaijapur.
--	Number of research station from MAU, Parbhani

Table 3.11: List of Seed agencies

Sr. No	Name of Seed Agency
1.	Maharashtra State Seed Corporation (M.S.S.C.)
2.	National Seed Corporation (N.S.C.)
3.	S.S. Darak and Sons Ltd, Jalna
4.	Mahyco Seeds Corporation Ltd, Jalna
5.	Nath Seeds Ltd, Aurangabad
6.	Pro-Agro Seeds Co. Ltd, Aurangabad
7.	Navbharat Seeds Pvt. Ltd, Jalna
8.	Durgeshwari Seeds Pvt. Ltd, Parbhani
9.	Balaji Seeds, Parbhani
10.	Ankur Seeds Pvt. Ltd, Nagpur
11.	Prawardhan Seeds , Hyderabad
12.	Padgilwar Agencies, Nagpur
13.	Palgare Seeds , Mehboob Nagar
14.	Zuari Agro Chemicals , Pune
15.	J. K. Industries Ltd, Nagpur
16.	Padamwar Agro Agencies, Nagpur
17.	Rallis India Ltd, Pune
18.	Tulsi Seeds Pvt. Ltd, Guntour
19.	Hindustan Seeds Company, Pune
20.	Indo-Chemical Hybrid Seeds , Pune
21.	Sandoz India Ltd, Pune
22.	Hindustan Siebagaigi Ltd, Mumbai
23.	Vasant Agro Chemical Ltd, Akola
24.	Virendra Krishi Seva Kendra , Osmanabad
25.	Bejo Sheetal Seeds Pvt. Ltd, Jalna

Baliraja Magazine (Jan 1998, Oct 1997, Dec 1997, Nov 1998, June 1998, July 1998, Sept 1998, Apr 1998).

Table 3.12: Name / URLs of consumer organization / NGOs

NAME	URLS
THANE SMALL SCALE INDUSTRIES ASSOCIATION	
KALYAN MANUFACTURERS' ASSOCIATION	
MAHAD MANUFACTURERS' ASSOCIATION	
MAHRATTA CHAMBER OF COMMERCE & INDUSTRY	http://www.mcciapune.com
AKHIL BHARTIYA GRAHAK PANCHAYAT	http://www.grahakpanchayat.org
GRAHAK PANCHAYAT	
VEEJ GRAHAK SANGH, PUNE	
VIDARBHA CHAMBER OF COMMERCE	
MARATHWADA INDUSTRIES ASSOCIATION	
MULLA PRAVARA CO-OP SOCIETY LTD	

Source: www.mercindia.com/otherlinks.htm

3.4.2 Information for Marketing and finance

Ultimately every thing boils down to economics. A farmer, trader and commission agent all would like to get maximum profit. Hence agricultural market system forms a very important subsystem. APMC are regulated marketing system established by government with the view to keep the farmer well informed about prices, sales and arrivals. The objective is to protect the farmer from uncertainties in the market.

Figure 3.1 shows organizational chart of APMC. Table 3.13 shows typical distances in between the markets. Logistics of MMCs and SMCs in Marathwada region is given in Table 3.14.

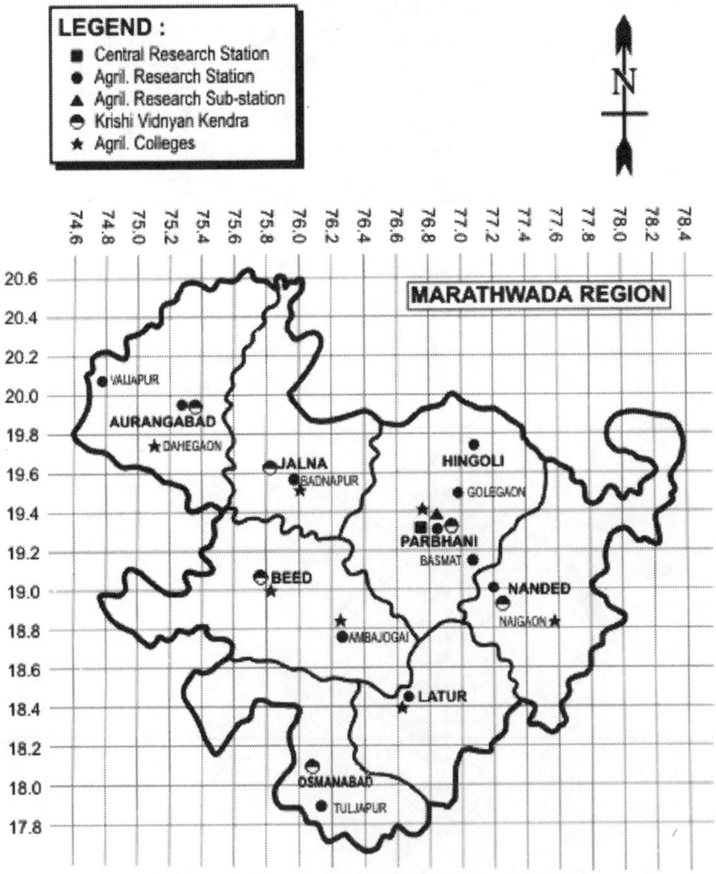

Map 4: Research and Educational institutions.
(For Agril. Schools: refer Table 3.10)

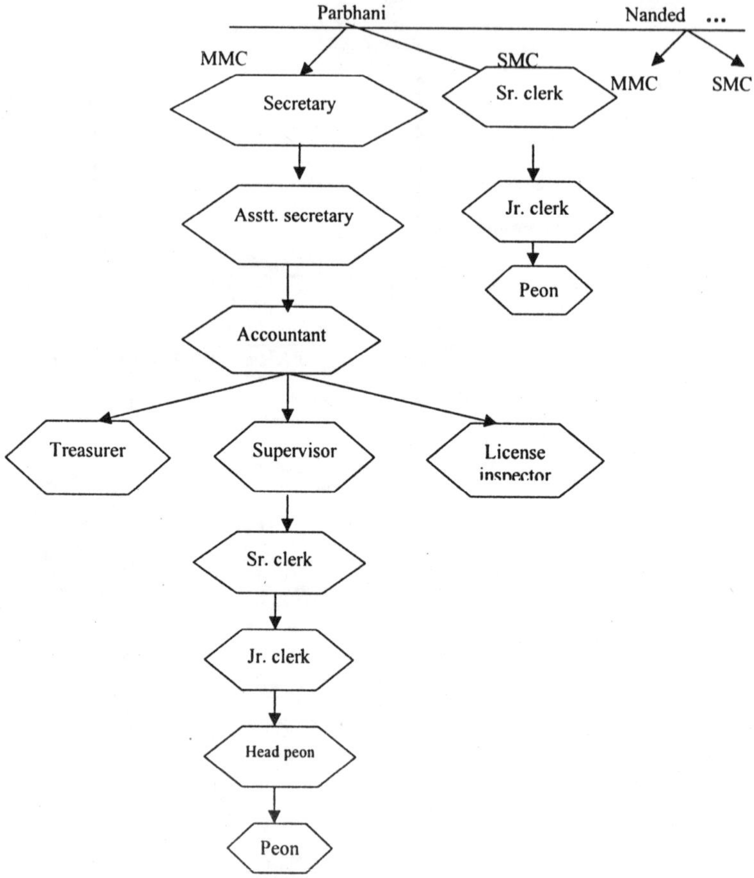

Figure 3.1: Organizational chart of Agricultural Produce Market Committee (APMC):

Table 3.13: Show distances in-between the markets

Place	Parbhani	Purna	Basmat	Jintur	Gangakhed	Manwat
Parbhani	0	40	40	42	39	65
Purna	40	0	70	82	72	103
Basmat	40	70	0	82	80	103
Jintur	40	70	80	0	80	103
Gangakhed	40	70	80	82	0	103
Manwat	40	103	103	82	103	0

Table 3.14 : Logistics of MMCs and SMCs

District	MMC	SMC
Aurangabad	6	16
Jalna	4	20
Parbhani	10	27
Beed	8	16
Nanded	11	28
Osmanabad	6	7
Latur	5	12
Total	***50***	***126***

Information from un-regulated market and information on insecticides, pesticides, fertilizers sale, seed sale, vegetable markets, animal bazaar all come under un-regulated markets is not covered in APMC information system.

A list of financial institutions in Marathwada which deal with agricultural finances is given in Table 3.15. Loans for farming, agro industries, and subsidies for various projects come under the preview of these institutions.

Table 3.15: Name of financial institutions in Marathwada

Name of district	Name of Bank
Aurangabad	Allahabad Bank, Andhra Bank, Abd. Dist. Central Co-op Bank (HO), Abd. Peoples Co-op Bank (HO), Bank of Baroda, Bank of India, Bank of Maharashtra, Bombay Mercantile Co-op Bank, Corporation Bank, Canara Bank, Central Bank of India, Dena Bank, Indian Overseas Bank, Janata Sahakari Bank, Maharashtra State Co-op Bank, Punjan National Bank, Punjab & Sind Bank, Sangli Bank, Saraswat Co-op Bank, State Bank of Hyderabad, State Bank of India, Syndicate Bank, Union Bank of India, UCO Bank, United Western Bank, Vijaya Bank, Vyasya Bank.
Beed	State Bank of India
Jalna	Andhra Bank, Bank of Baroda, Bank of India, Bank of Maharashtra, Central Bank of India, Dena Bank, Jalna Peoples' Co-op Bank, Sangli Bank, State Bank of Hyderabad, Syndicate Bank, Union Bank of India, United Western Bank

Name of district	Name of Bank
Latur	Andhra Bank, Bank of Baroda, Bank of India, Bank of Maharashtra, Central Bank of India, Dena Bank, Janata Sahakari Bank, Janata Sahakari Urban Bank, Osmanabad Dist. Central Co-op Bank(HO), Sangli Bank, State Bank of Hyderabad, Union Bank of India, United Western Bank
Nanded	Allahabad Bank, Bank of Baroda, Bank of India, Bank of Maharashtra, Bombay Mercantile Co-op Bank, Canara Bank, Central Bank of India, Dena Bank, Marathwada Gramin Bank, Nanded Dist. Central Co-op Bank(HO), Nanded Merchants Co-op Bank(HO), Punjab & Sind Bank, Punjab National Bank, Sangli Bank, State Bank of Hyderabad, State Bank of India, Syndicate Bank, Union Bank of India, United Western Bank, Vysya Bank.
Parbhani	Andhra Bank, Bank of Baroda, Bank of Maharashtra, Parbhani Dist. Central Co-op Bank (HO), Parbhani People's Co-op Bank (HO), Sangli Bank, Sangli Urban Co-op Bank, State Bank of Hyderabad, Union Bank of India.
Osmanabad	Allahabad Bank, Bank of Maharashtra, Canara Bank, Osmanabad Dist. Central Co-op Bank, Osmanabad Janata Sahakari Bank (HO), Osmanabad Urban Co-op Bank (HO), State Bank of Hyderabad.

Source: (1997 – 1998), Bank Directory, Suneja Publishers, New Delhi.

3.4.3 Information for Agro - industrial activities

Farmers, and businessmen need information about Agro industries like dal mills, oil mills, sugar mills, ginning mills, floor mills mainly in connection with selling raw material, processing of their farm produces. In turn the industries require maintaining information on availability of raw material, potential production, and growth trends of agricultural products.

3.4.4 Information for Seed industries

Seed is a major input in farming activities. Seed industries require information on demand of seeds, seed processing technology, seed availability. They have to monitor seed production activities and closely watch seed production programs on farmers' field. They also require information on breeding programs, new varieties development, new hybrids and so on. A list of seed industries is given in Table 3.11.

3.4.5 Information for Fertilizer Industries

Fertilizer Corporation of India, Zilha parishad are the main generators of information on demand and supply of fertilizers. Information on their distribution, consumption is very important. List of fertilizer companies is given in Table 3.16.

Table 3.16: List of Fertilizer agencies:

Sr. No	Name of Fertilizer Agency
1.	Rashtriya Chemical Fertilizer Ltd
2.	Indian Farmers Fertilizer Corporation (IFFCO)
3.	Krishak Bharti Corporation , (Kribhco) Gujarat
4.	Gujrat Fertilizer Corporation Ltd, (GFCL) Gujarat
5.	Zuari Industries Ltd, Goa
6.	Paradeep Phosphate Ltd, Orissa
7.	Deepak Fertilizers and Petro Chemicals Ltd, Pune
8.	Rallis India Ltd, Akola
9.	Gujarat State Fertilizer Company (G.S.F.C.) Gujarat
10.	Shiva Fertilizers Ltd, Nanded
11.	Rashi Fertilizer Ltd, Pune
12.	Raj Laxmi AgroTech India Ltd, Jalna
13.	Shri. Bhavani Fertilizer Ltd, Nanded
14.	Kisan National Fertilizer ltd, (NFL) Delhi
15.	Hymco Fertilizer Ltd, Jalna
16.	Liberty Phosphate Ltd, (LPL) Pune
17.	Parbhani Farmer Fertilizer Co-operative Ltd, Jintur
18.	Omex Agro Fertilizers Pvt. Ltd, Latur
19.	Mamde Fertilizers, Degloor
20.	Sanjay Krishi Seva Kendra, Latur

Baliraja Magazine (Jan 1998, Oct 1997, Dec 1997, Nov 1998, June 1998, July 1998, Sept 1998, Apr 1998).

3.4.6 Information for Pesticide and Insecticide industries

There are many pesticide and Insecticide companies in Marathwada. They are both users of information and generators of information. A list of pesticide and insecticide companies is given in Table 3.17.

Table 3.17: List of Insecticide or Pesticide agencies

Sr. No	Name of Insecticide Agency
1.	Maharashtra State Agril. Industrial Development Corporation, (M.A.I.D.C.) Aurangabad
2.	Ms. Pioneer Pvt. Ltd, New Delhi
3.	Ms. Shri. G. Pesticides Ltd, Wajedara, Gujarat
4.	Ms. Bangalore Pesticides Ltd, Bangalore
5.	Ms. Karamchand Appliances , New Delhi
6.	Ms. Bhaskar Agro Company Ltd, Hyderabad
7.	Ms. Tajlaxmi Agro Industries, Delhi
8.	Ms. Vallabh Pesticides Pvt. Ltd, Mumbai
9.	Ms. Hindustan Siebagaigi Ltd, Mumbai
10.	Ms. Vyankalesh Chemicals Pvt. Ltd, Hyderabad
11.	Ms. Vijayalaxmi Insecticides & Pesticides Ltd, Hyderabad
12.	Ms. Solar PharmChem Ltd, Gujarat
13.	Ms. Gujarat Agro Industries Corporation Ltd, Ahmedabad
14.	Ms. Pestichem India Ltd, Delhi
15.	Ms. Jahki Agencies , Hyderabad
16.	International Seeds Co. Ahmedabad
17.	Hindustan Lever Ltd, Hyderabad
18.	Universal Pestichem Industries Pvt. Ltd, Hyderabad
19.	United Pesticide , Raipur, Rajasthan
20.	Crophealth Pvt. Ltd, Ghaziabad (U.P.)
21.	Punjab Pesticide Industries Co-Society Ltd, Punjab
22.	Greencross Agro Chemicals Pvt. Ltd, Indaur
23.	Bharat Insecticide Ltd, New Delhi
24.	Agro Chemical Industries , Bangalore
25.	Indian Pesti-Control Co. Bhopal (M.P.)
26.	Sandoz India Ltd, Ahmedabad

Baliraja Magazine (Jan 1998, Oct 1997, Dec 1997, Nov 1998, June 1998, July 1998, Sept 1998, Apr 1998).

3.4.7 Information on weather and soils, suitability of soils

India meteorological department with weather stations spread all over the country are the main generators of weather information. The state agricultural universities, civil aviation authority of India also provide weather information. A well developed information system with VSAT connectivity between numbers of locations is already functional. Table 3.18 shows the list of VSATs.

Table 3.18: V-SAT Numbers :

(Total number of nodes = 69, Presently working = 66)
National Centre for medium range weather forecast.
(Meterology Department)

1) C-Dot Bangalore	21)	40) IARI, New Delhi
2) IMD Delhi	22) KKV, Dapoli	41)
3)	23)	42)
4)	24) ARS, Anandpur	43) ICAR, Imphal
5) ARS Udaypur	25) Hub station	44) RAU, Jaipur
6)	26) ARS, Kovilpati	45)
7) AAU, Jorhat (Asiam)	27) IGAU, Raipur	46) Shri Ganganagar
8) TNAU Coimbature	28) EAAS, Namakkal	47)
9)	29)	48) RARS Nagaon
10) C-Delhi	30)	49) CSAU, Kanpur
11) MBC, Chennai	31)	50)
12) NDAU, Faizabad	32)	51) UAS, Bangalore
13) PKV, Akola	33) UAS Bijapur	52) PRRI, Aduthurai
14) MAU, Parbhani	34)	53) RARS, Amblavay
15)	35) GAU, Anand	54) RARS, Pilicode
16) RAU, Pusa	36) GBPAUT, Ranichauri	55)
17) CASAM, Pune		56)
18) VAT Bhuwaneshwar	37)	57) Dantiwada
19) Kalayani	38)	58) RARS Jagtiyal
20)	39)	59)

60) RRS, Raichur	73)	87)
61) CEL Delhi	74) RARS, Diphu	88)
62)	75) ARS, Mulde	89) HPK, Palampur
63)	76)	90)
64) RSRS, Bharari	77) Bikaner Seobagh	91) C-DOT, Delhi
65)	78) HRS	92) AAS Jungagabh
66) KVK, Mathura	79)	93)
67)	80) DST, Delhi	94)
68) EAAS, Barapani	81)	95) PAU, Ludhiana
69)	82)	96)
70) Angraiu, Hyderabad	83) RRTTS, Keonghar	97) CAZRI, Jodhpur
	84)	98)
71)	85)	99) AAS Rahuri
72) Hub station	86) Jagdalpur	100)

Source : C-DOT Bangalore. DST organization Delhi

National Bureau of Soil Survey and Land Use Planning (NBSS&LUP):

It is one of the agencies where maps are generated. It is good source for remote sensing and processed maps. The responsibility of soil classification and land capability mapping lies with NBSS & LUP which is situated at Nagpur. The institute provides basic mapping services to department of agriculture, Maharashtra. NBSS & LUP in cooperation with the Department of Agriculture, initiated 'Soil Resource Mapping' of the state (on 1:250,000) during December 1986, using a 3-tier approach. The 3-tier approach involves image interpretation, ground/field surveys and lab analysis, and cartography and printing. The major objectives of NBSS & LUP are:

- To generate the soil resource map,
- To rationalize land use based on their capability,
- Soil-based research findings,

- To generate different thematic maps,
- To generate database for different mapped units for storage and retrieval

3.4.8 Information on Irrigation Projects and water availability

Irrigation is the most important aspect in system analysis. Hence Irrigation system forms very important subsystem. Table 3.19 shows major, medium and minor irrigation projects. Figure 3.2 shows organizational chart and of SDI. Figure 3.3 shows information flow diagram of SDI. Figure 3.4 shows decision diagram of allocation of water.

Table 3.19: Major, Medium and Minor irrigation projects

Major Projects	Medium projects	Minor projects
Jayakwadi (stage I), Jayakwadi (stage II), Upper Penganga, Manjra, Purna, Lower Godavari, Nandur Madhmeshwar, Lendi	Karpara, Masoli, ...	Pedgaon, Ambegaon, Rani Savargaon, Nakhatwadi, Takalwadi, Kodari, Tandulwadi, Devgaon, Jogwada, Belkheda, Vadali, chincholi, aadgaon, kehal, bhosi, charthana, kawad, mandwi, dahegaon, ghordari, sawana, babhulgaon, walki, suregaon, aundha, sendursena, purjal, wanjarwadi, pimpaldari, kokadhaba, keli, parola, wadad, chorjawala, hirdi, hadgaon, pimpri, kalamnuri, bothi, devdhari, dandegaon, pedgaon, padali, marsul, sawad ....
Total = 8	62	865

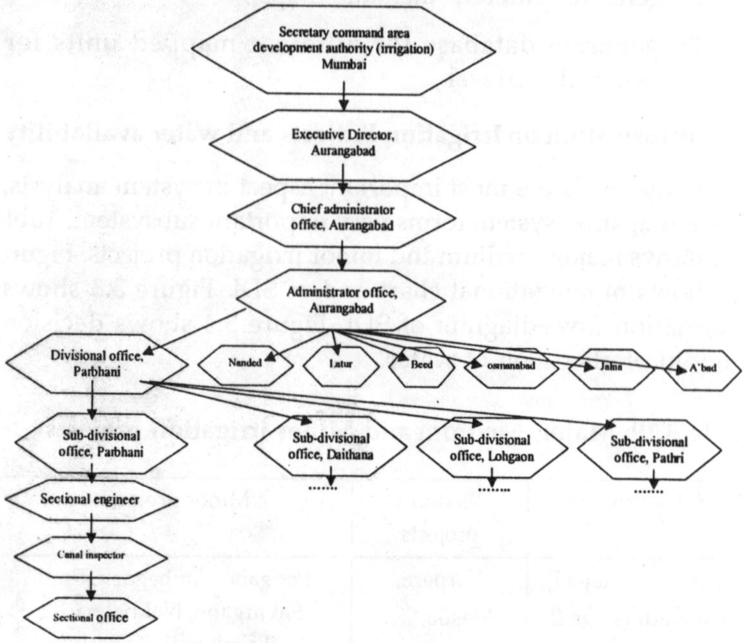

Figure 3.2: Organizational chart of State Department of Irrigation (SDI)

3.4.9 Information for Research and Education

No information system can survive without input from research workers. Extension workers at the best can be carriers of information. Through education there is a constant dissemination of information. Education in agriculture is imparted at various levels. Hence a system analysis of complete Education and Research system of Marathwada was taken up. Table 3.10 shows List of Agricultural colleges and Research stations in Marathwada region. Figure 3.5 shows organizational chart of Marathwada Agricultural University, which is one of the prime institutes responsible for agricultural education in the region. Map 4, Table 3.3 and Table 3.10 shows location of research station, number of researchers and students of agricultural colleges and schools, list of agricultural colleges and research stations respectively.

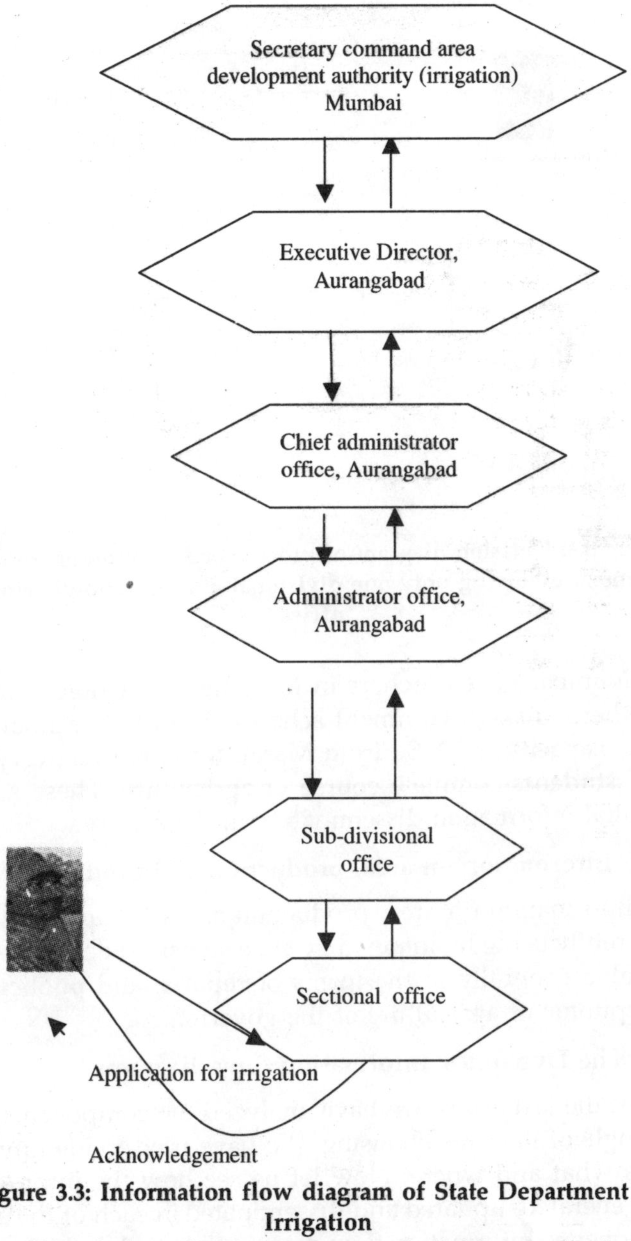

Figure 3.3: Information flow diagram of State Department of Irrigation (Only for one division and one sub-divisional office):

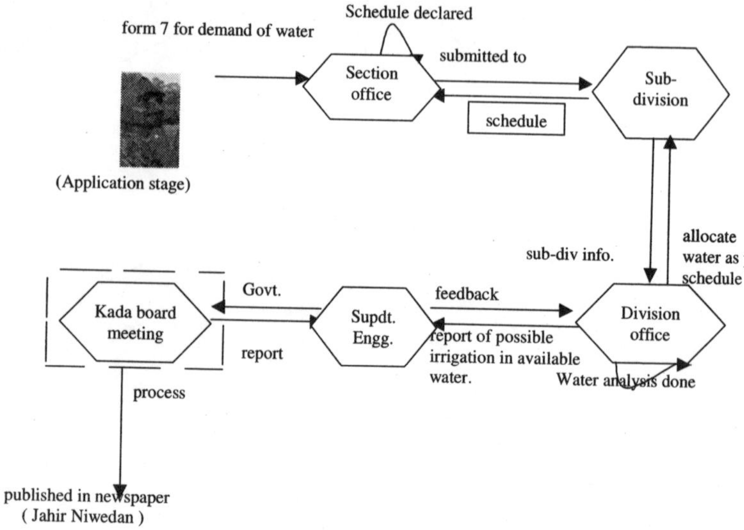

Figure 3.4: Decision diagram of process of allocation of water for farmers involving only one divisional and one•sub-divisional office

Number of researchers in Marathwada region is around 480, there are 5 government schools, 46 private schools and intake capacity is 60. So from Marathwada region every year 3,757 students complete course of agriculture. These are the potential information disseminators in the society.

3.4.10 Information on area, production and productivity

Information on area, production and productivity which is currently being maintained by state statistical departments is available generally in the forms of reports, and publications like epitome of agriculture of the government.

3.5 The Dynamics: information flow diagrams

In the last article we have analyzed the components from the angle of data warehousing. We have tried to identify who stores what and where. Now let us see how the information gets generated, updated and disseminated in each of the above components. Information flow diagrams depicting the paths of

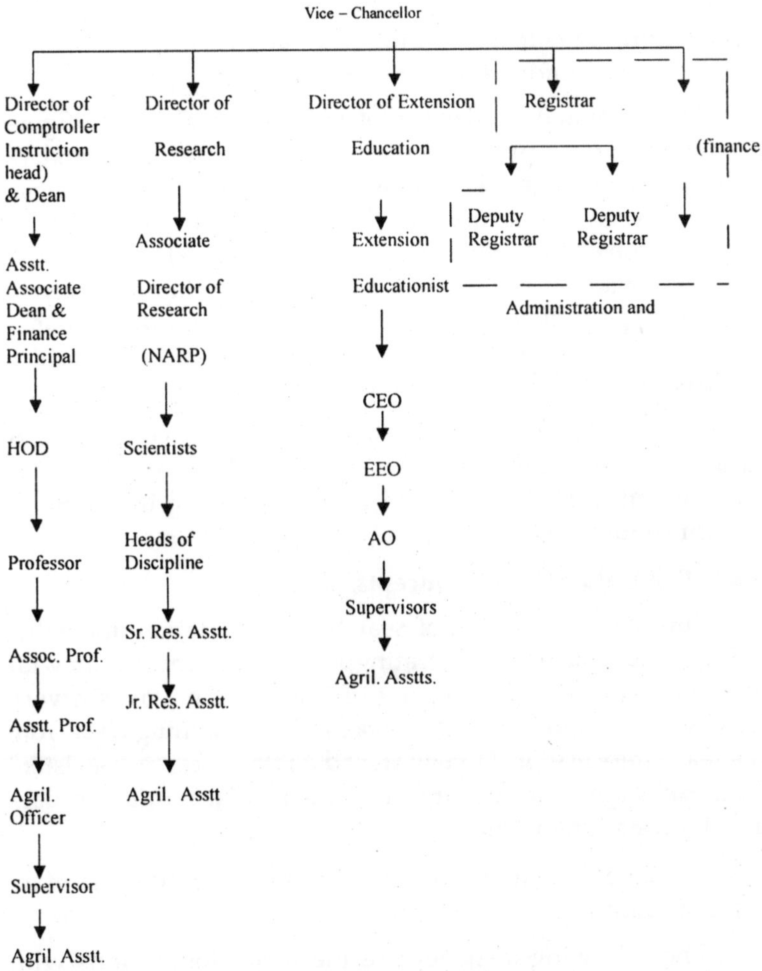

Figure 3.5: Organizational chart of Marathwada Agricultural University, Parbhani

Source: Digraskar (1996).

information flow, or in some cases cycle of information flow where feedback mechanism is very strong.

Figure 3.6 shows cycle of programme production and telecasting (Television), feedback and answer to queries through

TV programs. Figure 3.7 Shows cycle of Radio programme generation, broadcasting and feedback. Figure 3.8 shows possibilities of information flow through **Internet.**

Information flow diagram of T&V system shown in figure 3.9. Information is generated at top office in the form of booklets, CDs etc. The village extension worker acts as the direct contact point between the farmer and their jurisdiction. The feedback is pumped back into the system by VEW and AEO. The VEW and AEO also get information from agricultural university in the form of periodical trainings. Radio, television and newspaper also serves as sources of information for AEO and VEW which in turn deliver the information to needy users.

Figure 3.10 shows Information flow diagram of APMC. A farmer has to decide where to sell and when to sell, on the basis of information received from Marketing information system (figure 3.11).

3.6 The Data Mining Concepts

Surely current status of searching information under the existing multiplicity of generatingpoints of information in wide and unorganized warehousing of information leaves a very large gap in requirement and availability of mining data from the sea of information. Non-existent data structures, non-existent data exchange protocols are the fundamental hurdles in data and information mining.

3.7 Agencies/Organizations Established with the mandate for Data mining :

The following agencies are the major institutions with mandates for data mining for specific purposes.

T&V system of SDA, ATICs of Agricultural Universities, KVKs, Directorate of Extension in SAUs are the agencies established by the Govt. to do effective data mining from the warehouses like Meteorological Departments, NBSS&LUP, Govt. Statistical agencies and many other places. Not only that their mandate is to mine data, but they are further expected to convert mined data into useful information for the farming community and pass it on to them.

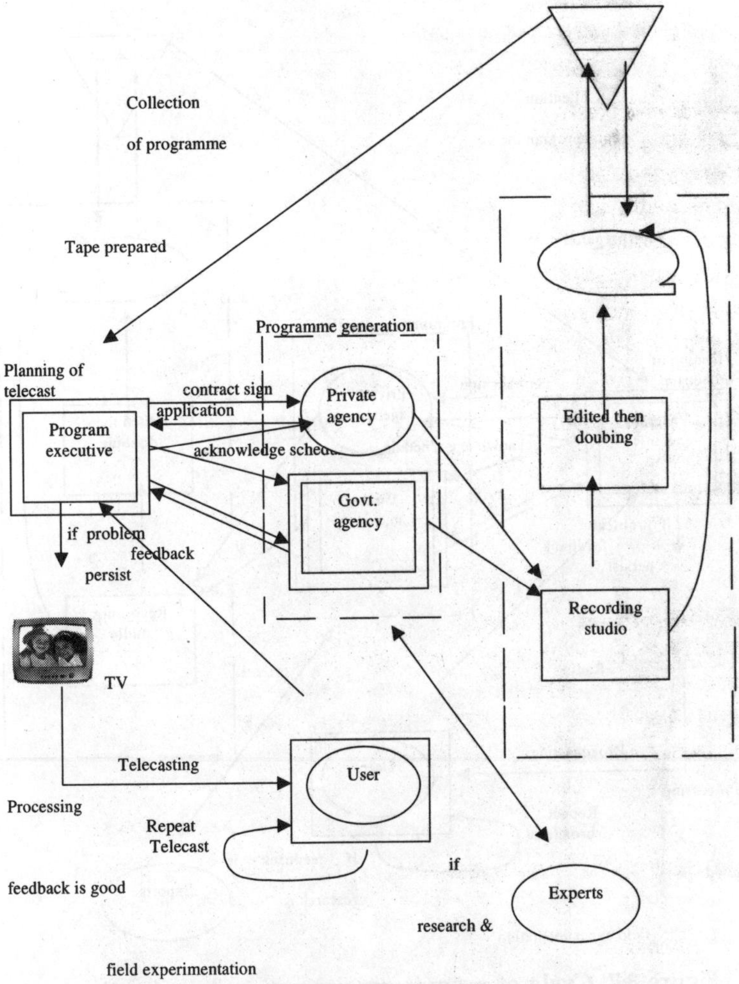

Figure 3.6: Programme production and telecasting.

Having completed the discussions on the system analysis, we will be discussing the concept of designing a Information in the next chapter.

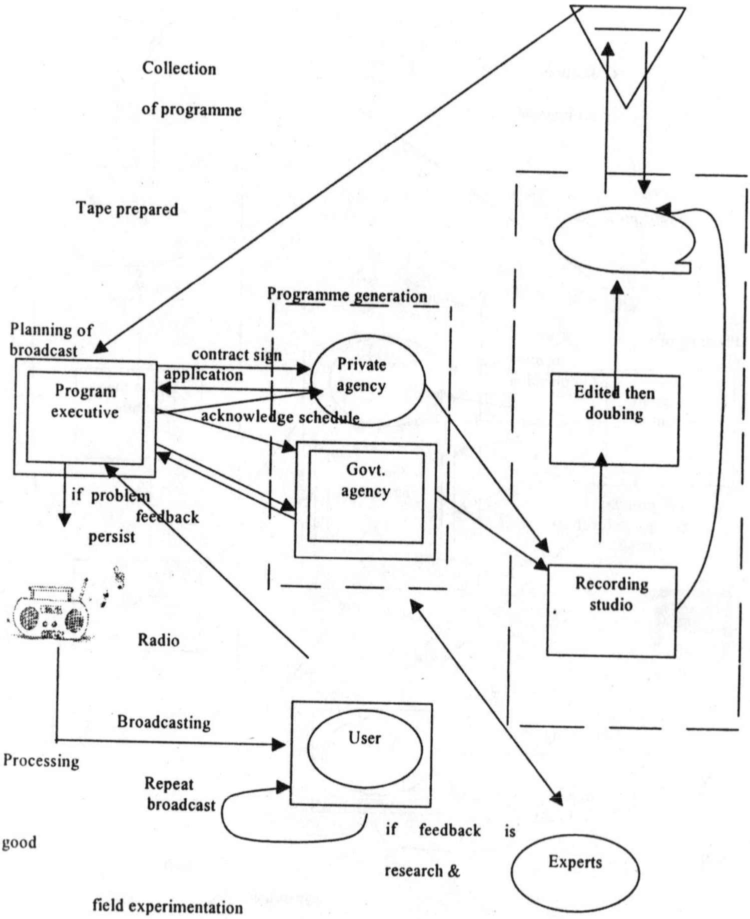

Figure 3.7: Cycle of programme generation, broadcasting and feedback.

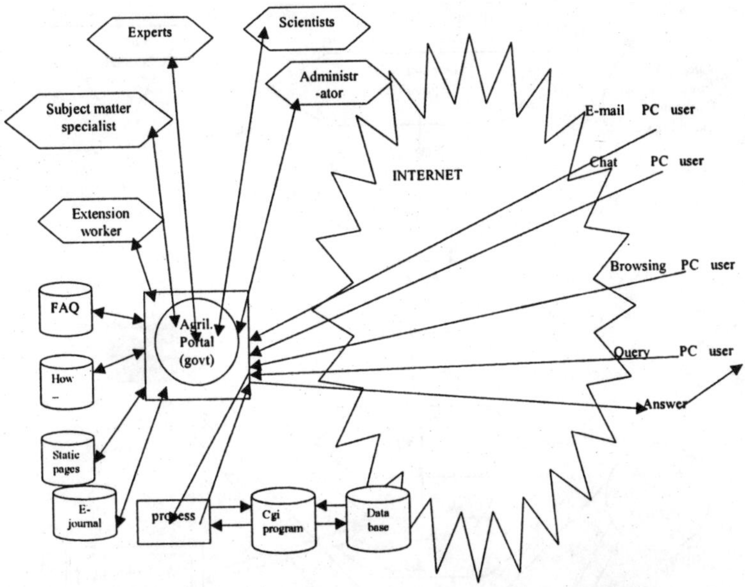

Figure 3.8: Possibilities of information flow through Internet.

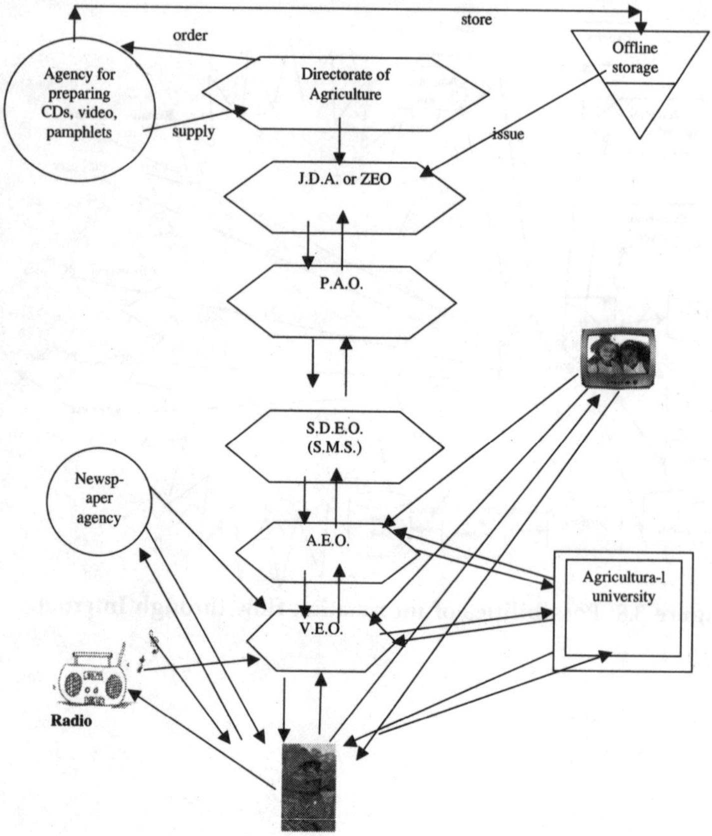

Figure 3.9: Information flow diagram of T&V system

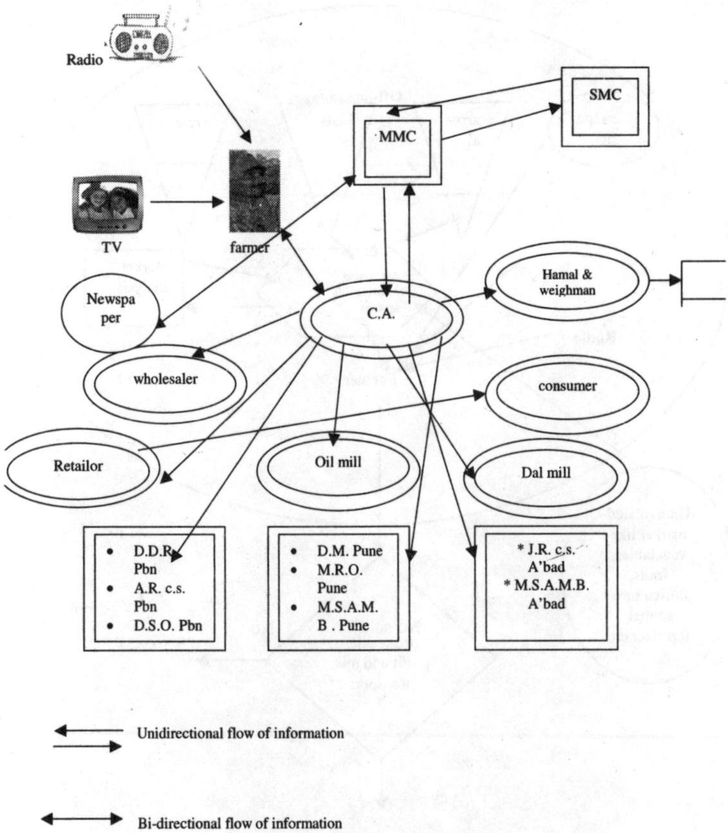

Figure 3.10: Information Flow diagram of APMC:

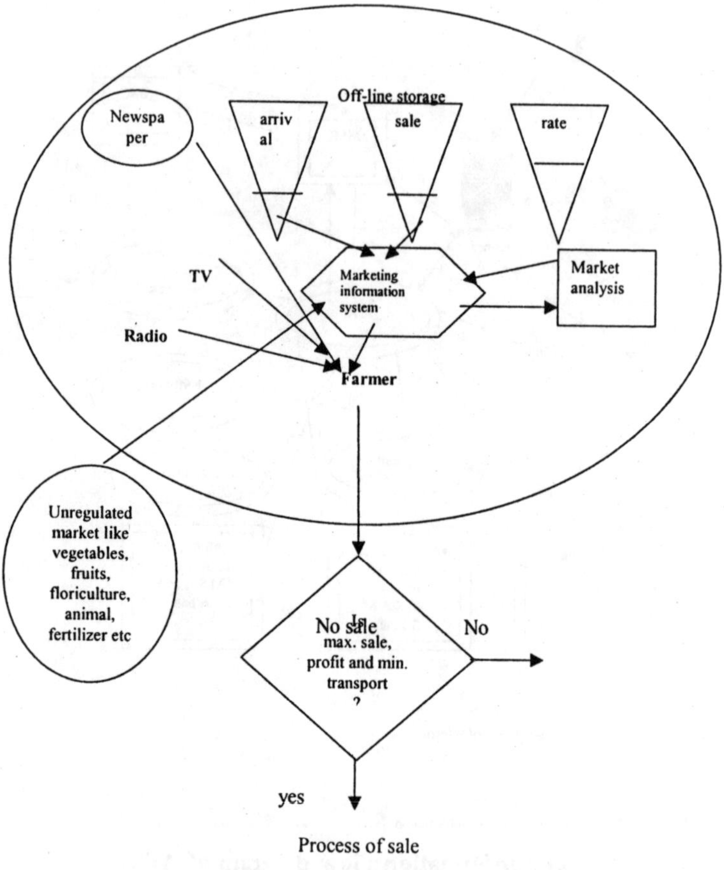

Figure 3.11: Decision Flow diagram of farmer

Chapter 4

Design of an Information System

4.0 Introduction

In this chapter, we will discuss the model designs of Agricultural Information Systems in general. Before we do that first we define an Agricultural Information System (AIS).

4.1 Definition of Agro Information System

Various others have defined Management Information System (Davis and Olson (1984)) and Geographical Information System (GIS) (Heywood et. al. (2000)). It is evident that a precise definition of information systems is not always possible because the system could be designed for objectives varying in nature. However, we have attempted to give a broad definition of AIS here.

> *Agro Information System (AIS) is an integrated collection of hardware, software and communication media capable of manipulating, update, analyze, store, capture and display data in various organizations like State Department of Agriculture, State Department of Irrigation, Agricultural Universities, food and Agro-based industries, Marketing organizations, and specially geographically referenced information on soil classification, meteorological information, transport and marketing facilities, programs helpful for problem solving and decision-making and running advisory services for agricultural planners, research workers, farmers, extension workers, businessmen alike.*

Depending on the targeted users or objectives, it may form a combination of Management Information System (MIS) and Geographical Information System (GIS) in its largest form or it could be a simple MIS only or in its smallest form. Unlike industries who require MIS, planners who require GIS, extension workers require an advisory system. By an advisory system we mean a facility using which extension worker can help farmers in better agriculture and proper marketing. Though we have defined an AIS the concept would not become clear unless we compare the mechanism of generation of information, dissemination of information and use of information under an IT based environment with the current non-IT based situation. We have attempted such an comparison in the following table.

Comparison between existing communication channel and IT enabled information system:

Tables 4.1 to 4.6 show basic difference between the traditional information system and the IT enabled system proposed. As it can be seen that fundamentally there is no difference in the two systems. The major difference is that the modern communication tools and IT tools improve upon the existing system tremendously.

Table 4.1: Comparison between existing communication channel of radio and television station and what it should be in Information Technology (IT) based system:

Traditional process of programme compilation	Modern IT based requirement of tool
Application from any expert to programme coordinator	On-line form processing tool
Willingness from programme coordinator	E-mail
Call for recording	E-mail
Recording a programme, if problem persists, editing and doubing is needed	Recording software, editing and doubing software
Acknowledge the date and time of programme to the expert	E-mail
Broadcast by radio or television station	Broadcast by Internet

Table 4.2: Comparison between existing communication of extension worker & farmer and what it should be in IT enabled system

Traditional process of communication	IT based communication
Extension worker went to village	Chat session
Extension worker contacted to limited number of farmers	
Bi-directional communication takes place to solve queries of farmers	
Extension worker back to office	

Table 4.3: Comparison between display of charts & posters and what it should be in IT enabled system

Traditional process of displaying charts and posters	IT based process of displaying charts and posters
Collect photos using survey	Collect photos and scan using scanner & digitize it
Editing photos	Image editing if required, add titles and sub-titles
Farmers gathered at one place	Farmers can access in Internet café
Display using slide projection or Direct projection	Display on PC with multimedia kit. For specific presentation LCD projector can be used to project on large wall

Table 4.4: Comparison between training to extension worker and what it should be in IT enabled system

Traditional process of training to Extension worker	IT based process of training to Extension worker
Communicate to Extension worker for training	Announcement on Web page
Willingness to accept for training	E-mail
Preparation of training at training centre	Presentation of training on PC
Acknowledge of schedule of training	E-mail
Bi-directional communication takes place between trainees and trainer	PC with video conferencing system using Internet and input device for 1:1 communication

Table 4.5: Comparison between seminar or conference or workshop and what it should be in IT enabled system:

Traditional process of arranging seminar or conference or workshop	IT based process of arranging seminar or conference or workshop
Identification of speakers	Database of speakers
Willingness of speaker	E-mail
Acknowledgement to speaker	E-mail
Announcement in newspaper	Advertisement on web page
Willingness of participation	E-mail
Acknowledgement of schedule	E-mail
Seminar is imparted and bi-directional communication takes place	PC with video conferencing system using Internet and input device for 1:1 communication

Table 4.6: Comparison between print media and what it should be in IT enabled system:

Traditional process of publication of articles	Modern IT based publication of articles
Article submitted to editorial board from any expert	E-mail
Willingness of acceptance or rejection of article	E-mail
Article send back to expert if correction is needed	E-mail
Editing of article	Editing software
As per type of article, published in newspaper, magazines, books, research bulletin etc	Articles may be stored on Hard disk, tape, CDs
Finally available to any user	User obtain on PC using Internet connection

4.2 Different models of AIS:

Considering the needs and objectives of under different possible situations we have identified five possible models of

AIS. They are defined on the basis of their architecture.

- Design specification 1: Information system run by an individual expert, free web space, dial-up based (ISEFWSD):

  Architecture:

  Server: Not required,

  Web space: To be obtained from free web space providers,

  Network: Not required,

  Internet connectivity: PC with dial-up connection.

  Scope: This type of designis suitable for individual experts like agronomist, soil scientist, horticulturist, floriculturist, sugar specialist, seed specialist etc who may have limited clientele and who would like to run an information system for their benefit. Such a system would be basically a personal consultancy service.

- Design specification 2: Information system run by educational institute / small organizations / small industry, hired web space, dial-up based (ISOHWSD):

  Architecture:

  Server: Not required,

  Web space: To be hired on rent from web space providers,

  Network: Not required,

  Internet connectivity: PC with dial up connection.

  Scope: This type of design is suitable for krishi vidyan kendras, krishi seva kendras, private or government colleges or small-scale industry people who would like to run an information system.

- Design specification 3: Information system run by a large organization / large industry, stand alone server with LAN, leased line-based (ISLOSLL):

Architecture:

Server: Stand-alone server,

Network: LAN,

Internet connectivity: Leased line based.

Scope: This type of design is suitable for government organizations or any university which may have a headquarter and offices connected to headquarter by LAN and also providing Intranet environment.

- Design specification 4: Information system run by large organization / large industry, stand alone server with LAN, VSAT based (ISLOSLV):

  Architecture:

  Server: Stand-alone server,

  Network: LAN,

  Internet connectivity: VSAT based.

Scope: This type of design is suitable for large organizations or large industry that may have connectivity with LAN and also providing Intranet environment.

- Design specification 5: Information system run by very large organization / large industry, Multi-servers in a network environment with LAN / WAN, VSAT based (ISLOMLWV):

  Architecture:

  Server: Multi-servers in a network environment,

  Network: LAN / WAN,

  Internet connectivity: VSAT based.

Scope: This type of design is suitable for State Department of Agriculture, State Department of Irrigation, and Statutory Agricultural Universities etc by LAN or WAN and also providing Intranet environment.

These models will be discussed in detail one by one now.

4.3 Procedure of Design specifications 1 and 2:

Design specifications 1 and 2 are the smallest possible designs. They depend on web spaces provided by external agencies. Hence facilities that can be created are very restrictive.

Detailed specifications and requirements:

- PC with Dial up line,
- Registration on free web hosting server or leased space based server,
- Hardware selection as under

CPU:	Choose CPU from table 4.7
RAM:	128 MB or more SDRAM
Video:	Standard SVGA
Multimedia:	Required.
Extra:	Modem 56.6 kbps or more,

- Software selection: any common operating system which generally contains tools for web page development like Front page, XML and so on.

Design of Information content:

- It should contain the following static pages:

1. Newsletter (weekly or bi-weekly),
2. Contact address of advisory service,
3. Client information (Names and contact addresses),
4. Tips in the forms of FAQs and HowTos.

- With the help of the space provider, few dynamic facilities like on-line registration, news groups can also be maintained for the benefit of the clients.

Humanware:

The owner will be the system administrator and subject matter specialist or expert.

Advantages:

1. It is very cheap because of the minimum infrastructure requirement,

2. It can disseminate information freely anywhere in the world,
3. Maintenance of web site done by service provider.

Disadvantages:

1. Security is minimum,
2. There is constraint on creation of dynamic facilities.
3. Because of space limitation, it is suitable for only small information system.

Table 4.7: List of recent CPU availability

CPU	*As on*
AMD Athlon XP 3200+ 'Barton' is bumped to a 400 MHz bus.	AMD May 13, 2003
AMD Athlon MP 2800+	AMD May 6, 2003
Intel Pentium 4-M @ 2.5 GHz; Mobile Celeron @ 1.26 & 2.2 GHz	Intel April 16, 2003
Intel Pentium 4 @ 3 GHz	Intel April 14, 2003
Intel Celeron @ 2.3, 2.4 GHz	Intel March 31, 2003
AMD Athlon XP 2500+, 2800+, 3000+ ' Barton' is unveiled with double the L2 cache.	AMD February 10, 2003
AMD Athlon MP 2600+	AMD February 4, 2003
Intel Pentium 4-M @ 2.4 GHz; Pentium-III M @ 900 & 933 MHz Mobile Celeron @ 800, 866 & 2000 MHz	Intel January 14, 2003
AMD Athlon MP 2400+	AMD December 12, 2002
A) Intel RAID controller SRCU42L:- The Intel® RAID Controller SRCU42L offers the latest SCSI technology, Ultra320, in a low-profile form factor for high-density server applications. Featuring the Intel® 80303 I/O processor, the Intel RAID Controller	--

CPU	*As on*
SRCU42L includes two Ultra320 SCSI channels (one internal and one external)-- supporting up to 30 SCSI devices (15 per channel). This feature-rich RAID controller enables you to deliver storage solutions with very high availability and enhanced data protection.	
B) Intel RAID controller SRCU42L:- The Intel® RAID Controller SRCS14L provides full-featured RAID data protection for entry-level servers. As one of the first hardware-based Serial ATA (SATA) RAID cards in the market, and the first four-port, low-profile adapter to use an I/O processor, the RAID controller SRCS14L enables system builders to implement robust SATA hardware RAID data protection in a rapid time-to-market and at a very low cost per megabyte.	--
C) RAID server: Powerful Features to Deliver Versatile Growth in Servers and Workstations: Deliver the performance, quality, and reliability that are vital for both server and workstation applications using the Intel® Server Board SE7505VB2. With dual Intel® Xeon™ processors, a 533MHz system bus, and the Intel® E7505 chipset, the powerful and versatile Server Board SE7505VB2 enables you to create a broad range of systems that deliver high-end processing to solutions ranging from entry-level to enterprise-critical. The Intel® Server Board SE7505VB2 extends the bandwidth and performance- enhancing features of Intel® NetBurst™ microarchitecture and Intel® Hyper-Threading Technology in a package ideally suited to the unpredictable computing demands of growing businesses.	---

CPU	As on
D) Non – stop Himalaya S-series server and chain management (Tandem server) : Tandem Service Management (TSM) screens for server configuration, data paths, 8 and 16 CPU server configuration option, Introduction to SCF, Use SCF commands to identify server.	--

http://www.cpuscorecard.com/arch_news.htm

http://www.intel.com/design/servers/buildingblocks/boards.htm (source of A,B,C)

http://education.hp.com/datasheets/U4167S.pdf (source of D).

4.4 Procedure of Design specifications 3 and 4:

Design specification3 and 4 are the largest possible designs. They can obtain required bandwidth from different Internet Service Providers (ISP).

Detailed specifications and requirements:

- Server,
- Registration of web site,
- Selection of ISP

1. For leased line: RAD modem, router, telephone connection.(Fig 4.1)
2. For VSAT: Antenna, Indoor unit (IDU-router) (Fig 4.2)

- Hardware selection (server)

  CPU: Choose CPU from table 4.7

  Interface card: SCSI card.

  RAM: 256 MB or more SDRAM

  Video: Standard SVGA

  NIC: Network card with local buffer memory,

- LAN and cable connectivity (Table 4.8 and Table 4.9),
- Client machines: PCs / diskless client,
- Software selection: Network platforms and application software to be selected from Table 4.10 and for security software from Table 4.11

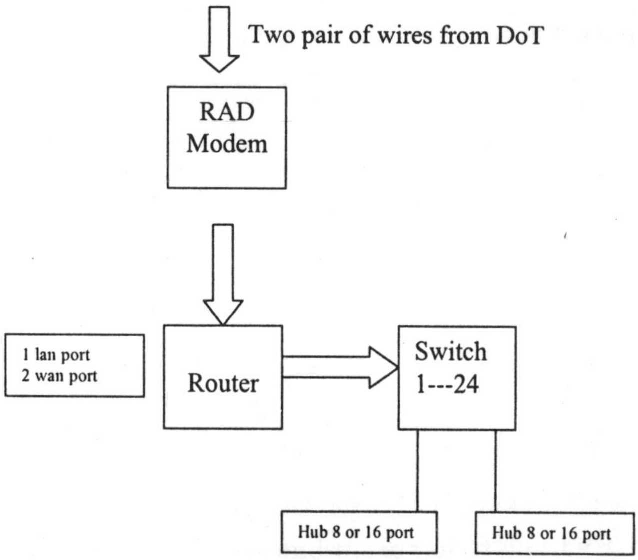

Router: 10 Mbps / Half duplex (Ethernet), Leased line speed: 64 Kbps
Type of proxy: Analog X.
Type of connection (Serial or Hub): Intel switch.
IP addresses : 16 (first & last not used).

Figure 4.1: Leased line connection

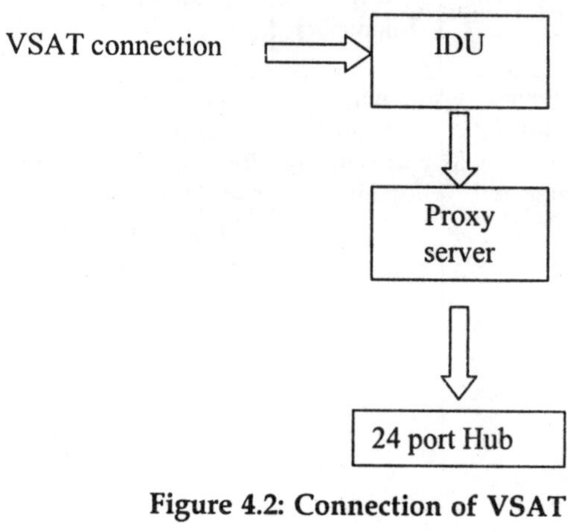

Figure 4.2: Connection of VSAT

Table 4.8: Classification of interconnected processors by scale

Interprocessor distance	*Processors located in same*	*Example*
0.1 m	Circuit board	Data flow machine
1 m	System	Multi-computer
10 m	Room	Local area network
100 m	Building	
1 km	Campus	
10 km	City	Metropolitan area network
100 km	Country	Wide area network
1000 km	Continent	
10000 km	Planet	The Internet

Tanenbaum(2001), Computer Networks. PHI, new Delhi-1

Table 4.9: Various factors or attributes for comparing the major media

	Twisted pair wire	*Baseband coaxial cable*	*Broadband coaxial cable*	*Fibre optic cable*
Topologies supported	Ring, Star, Bus, tree bus, tree	Ring, Bus, Tree	Bus, Tree	Ring, Star, Tree
Maximum number of nodes	Generally up to 1024	Generally up to 1024	Generally up to 1024	Generally up to 1024
Maximum geographical	3 Kilometers	10 Kilometers	50 Kilometers	10 Kilometers and up
Type of signal	Single-channel, unidirectional, analog and digital, depending on type of modulation used, half or full-duplex	Single-channel, bidirectional, digital, half duplex	Multi-channel, unidirectional RF analog, half-duplex (full duplex can be achieved by using two cables or two channels)	Single-channel, unidirectional, half duplex, single encoded light beam per fibre (full duplex can be achieved by using two fibre)

	Twisted pair wire	*Baseband coaxial cable*	*Broadband coaxial cable*	*Fibre optic cable*
Maximum bandwidth	Generally up to 4 Mbps	Generally up to 10 Mbps	Up to 499 MHz (aggregate total)	Generally up to 50 Mbps in 10 Km
Major advantages	* Low cost may be existing plant. * No wiring needed. * Very easy to install.	* Low maintenance cost. * Very easy to install.	* Support voice, data and video application. * Better immunity to noise and interference than baseband. * More flexible topology.	* Support voice, data and video application simultaneously. * Better immunity to noise crosstalk and electric interference. * Very high bandwidth. * Highly secure. * Low signal loss. * Low weight. * Highly durable.
Major disadvantages	* High error rates at higher speeds. * Low immunity to noise, crosstalk and electric interference * Limited bandwidth. * Security is low. * Difficult to maintain, troubleshoot.	* Low immunity to noise, crosstalk than broadband. * Bandwidth can carry only 40% of load. * Limited distance and topology.	* High maintenance cost. * Difficult to install. * RF modems are required at each station.	* Very high cost. * Require skilled installation and maintenance personnel. * Experimental technology. * Currently limited to point to point connection.

	Twisted pair wire	*Baseband coaxial cable*	*Broadband coaxial cable*	*Fibre optic cable*
Bandwidth	Low	Moderate	High	Very high
Data transfer reliability	Low	High	High	Very high
Noise susceptibility	High	Moderate	Low	None
Transmission security	Low	Low	Low	High
Length	Low	Moderate	High	Very high
Installation	Easiest	Hard	Hardest	Moderate

(May1997), Computer communication/ ADIT,CDAC, Pune.

Table 4.10: Operating system and its corresponding web servers:

Operating System	Web Server	Databases	Tools	Models for which suitable
Windows 98	Personal Web Server (Xiatami)	Ms-Access, Sql server	Ms-office, C, C++, Visual Studio etc	Design specification 1,2
Windows 2000	Personal Web Server	Ms-Access, Sql server	Ms-office, C, C++, Visual Studio etc	Design specification 1,2
Windows Millennium	Personal Web Server	Ms-Access, Sql server	Ms-office, C, C++, Visual Studio etc	Design specification 1,2
Windows XP	Personal Web Server	Ms-Access, Sql server	Ms-office, C, C++, Visual Studio etc	Design specification 1,2
Windows NT	Internet Information Server	Ms-Access, Sql server	Ms-office, C, C++, Visual Studio etc	Design specification 3,4
Linux	Apache Web Server	PostGre Sql server, MySql server	StarOffice, C, C++, HTML etc	Design specification 3,4
Sun	ONE web server	PostGre Sql server, MySql server	StarOffice, C, C++, HTML etc	Design specification 5

Table 4.11: List of Security software (Firewall softwares)

Security software	Security software
Socks	Tcpr
TCP Wrapper	TIS Firewall Toolkit
Xp-BETA	--

http://www.alw.nih.gov/Security/prog-firewall.html

<u>Design of Information content:</u>

- It should contain the following static pages:
    1. Newsletter (weekly or bi-weekly),
    2. Scientific / extension journal (quarterly or half yearly),
    3. List of experts and links to them,
    4. Links to other important sites,
    5. Tips in the forms of FAQs and HowTos.
- It should contain the following dynamic facilities:
    1. Membership registration,
    2. Form processing tools,
    3. Mail service for members,
    4. Chat sessions,
    5. Video conferencing facilities,
    6. Expert systems,
    7. Simulations, simulation tools, statistical analysis, projections,
    8. Maps and tools for analysis (GIS).

Humanware:

- System administrator,
- Web designers,
- Programmers,
- Subject matter specialists / experts.

Advantages:

1. It can disseminate information anywhere in the world,
2. No noise,
3. 100 percent reachability,

4. Full faith,
5. Suitable for large organizations / large industries which wish to run information services.

Disadvantages:

1. Lack of Internet facility in rural areas.

4.5 Procedure of Design specification 5:

It is the very large design of an organization or industry. It can obtain required bandwidth from different Internet Service Providers (ISP).

Detailed specifications and requirements:

- Server,
- Registration of web site,
- Selection of ISP.

  For VSAT: Antenna, Indoor unit (IDU-router) (Fig 4.2)
- Hardware selection (server)

  CPU: Choose CPU from table 4.7

  Interface card: SCSI card.

  RAM: 512 MB or more SDRAM

  Video: Standard SVGA

  NIC: Network card with local buffer memory,
- LAN and cable connectivity (Table 4.8 and Table 4.9),
- Servers connected to each other by LAN and WAN,
- Client machines: PCs / diskless client,
- Software selection: Network platforms and application software to be selected from Table 4.10 and for security software from Table 4.11

<u>Design of Information content:</u>

- It should contain the following static pages:
  1. Newsletter (weekly or bi-weekly),
  2. Scientific / extension journal (quarterly or half yearly),
  3. List of experts and links to them,

4. Links to other important sites,
5. Tips in the forms of FAQs and HowTos,

- It should contain the following dynamic facilities:

1. Membership registration,
2. Form processing tools,
3. Mail service for members,
4. Chat sessions,
5. Video conferencing facilities,
6. Expert systems,
7. Simulations, simulation tools, statistical analysis, projections,
8. Maps and tools for analysis (GIS).

Humanware:

- System administrator,
- Web designers,
- Programmers,
- Subject matter specialists / experts.

Advantages:

1. It can disseminate information anywhere in the world,
2. No noise,
3. 100 percent reachability,
4. Full faith,
5. Suitable for very large organizations / very large industries which wish to run information services.

Disadvantages:

1. Lack of Internet facility in rural areas.

4.6 Tools room

We have tried to identify and enlist some of the software tools which are required to be incorporated while designing an Information system. The choice may vary from situation to situation.

1) *Search Engines:*

Search engines are required for quick information search at the time of browsing. These are generally developed using development tools or using scripting languages. One special instance is the search engine we have developed in the Advisory System, required for establishing question-answer session. A specific instance of use of such a tool is given in Chapter 5. In few websites, search facility is available. When we will provide keywords, it gives choice either to search from World Wide Web or from the same server.

2) *Statistical Tools:*

Time series analysis is mainly required in Marketing information system where one is concerned about changes in seasonal and temporal changes in sales, arrivals and prices.

a) *Trend Estimators:*

They are required to show trend of past history.

b) *Trend Generators:*

They are required to project future trends.

Specific tools developed in this area are given in Chapter 6.

3) *Simulators:*

Simulation software should be capable to show future behavior in numeric or graphic format, growth rate of one or more components and its uncertainty.

a) Future behavior in numeric or graphic format
b) Growth rate of one or more variables
c) Uncertainty of one or more variables

4) *GIS software:*

They are required to show soil classification maps, watershed maps, forest area maps, river maps, irrigation maps, land use planning maps etc. GIS softwares like Grass, Spring, GeoMedia, Arc/Info can be used for this purpose.

5) *User requirement tools:*

These tools are generally required for the following in any

dynamic page. These are essentially CGI processes.

a) Login ID verification

b) Accepting forms

c) Processing forms

d) Report generation.

6) Chat session establishment

Under this immediate bi-directional communication takes place between expert and user. Special software available on server side as well as client side. Softwares like Game voice server, Parachat, Linn software chat room.

7) Videoconferencing facility

This is useful for conducting on-line training programmes, on-line farmers advisory sessions. Hence it is very useful for extension workers. However this requires availability of web camera and video conferencing software at both ends. One can choose from the following software like Forum software, Message board software.

8) Mail tools

Mail server configuration on server side and providing space to users are the main things to be done. Special software like Secure mail server, Merak mail server are available for this purpose.

9) E - Finance tools

For money transactions using the system, this tool is required. Software required is Award winning finance software (www.icode.com).

4.7 Client / Server model:

4.7.1 Server hardware architecture:

The focus on two widely popular hardware architecture features - Reduced Instruction Set Computer (RISC) and Symmetric Multiprocessing (SMP) architecture.

In general, these factors include CPU architecture, the size and implementation methods of the instruction set, the ability of compilers to optimize for performance, computer chip technology and the operating system.

Compilers and Operating Systems, therefore, should be capable of exploiting the hardware architecture to achieve the highest possible performance. Computer performance can be described by the following symbolic formula:

Performance = 1 / [(cycle time) * (path length) * (cycles / instruction)]

Where, the cycle time is the opposite of the system clock rate and is mostly limited by underlying chip technology.

Path length describes the number of machine instructions necessary to execute one command. The shorter the path length, the higher the resulting performance.

Cycles / instruction factor describes how many computer cycles are necessary to execute one instruction. If the number is less than 1, then more than one instruction can be executed in one CPU cycle. Thus, performance is better.

4.7.2 RISC Vs CISC:

In RISC architecture, instructions are decoded directly by the hardware, thus increasing the speed of the processing.

Originally, RISC processor contained only the simplest instruction extracted from a Complex Instruction Set Computer (CISC) architecture, and hardware was optimized for these instructions. IBMs RS/6000 is an example of the super scalar RISC implementation.

Another innovation in the RISC architecture is super pipelining. Pipelining is a technique that allows more than one instruction to be processed simultaneously.

4.7.3 Symmetric Multiprocessing:

As CPU costs are decreasing, users find that adding processors to their existing multiprocessor hardware is significantly more economical than either adding computer systems or replacing existing systems with more powerful uniprocessor systems. Adding or replacing uniprocessors has its drawbacks:

1) Adding processors usually results in addition of expensive peripheral devices.
2) Stand alone uniprocessors cannot share memory, unless they are networked at additional expense. Nor can they speed up applications, unless applications are distributed at additional cost and complexity.
3) Adding faster uniprocessors is more expensive than obtaining the same performance by increasing the number of processors.

Thus, multiprocessor - based systems provide the ability to increase performance incrementally.

There are two generic types of the multiprocessor systems:

- A loosely - coupled or Distributed Memory Multiprocessor: incorporates a large number of self - sufficient processors, each with its own operating system and resources (memory, disk etc. The processors communicate over networks and I/O channels, which makes interprocessor communication and cooperation dependent on network and I/O channel performance and throughput, and, therefore, relatively slow.
- A tightly - coupled or Shared Memory Multiprocessor: consists of a relatively small number of processors that share a common memory, common operating system, common I/O, and various other system resources. Processors select tasks to be executed from a common task pool, and are interconnected via a high speed common system bus, thereby providing extremely efficient interprocessor communications.

Of these two generic multiprocessor types, only shared memory multiprocessors provide true scalable performance at a low cost.

4.7.4 Functions of Client / Server model:

File sharing: In a workgroup environment, clients may have a need to share the same data file.

Printer sharing: In a workgroup environment, one high capacity printer may replace all individual client printers.

Database access: Database servers provide clients with access to data that resides on a server. DBMSs provide concurrent data access with various levels of locking granularity and data integrity.

Communication services: In a workgroup environment that is connected to remote host processor, all communications software and hardware can be concentrated on special communication server, to which clients may forward their communication requests for processing.

Facsimile services: That usually require special equipment and software, are now more frequently trusted to dedicated fax servers.

Multi-user support: Even in a small workgroup environment, a server should be able to service multiple concurrent clients.

Scalability: As the number of applications, their resource requirements, and number of users grow, a server should be able to satisfy these increasing demands on its resources i.e., should provide scalable performance.

Performance: A server system should provide performance levels satisfactory to the business needs and user requirements in a Multiuser Client / server environment.

Storage: As the number of users and applications running on a server increases, and as advances in storage technology drive the costs of physical storage down, the demand for extra storage and faster access times becomes one of the critical requirements for a server system.

Multimedia: Image, video and sound applications are becoming more and more popular. So, the requirements for a server system may include the ability to store not only digitized images on disk, but also hypertext on an optical storage device - Write - Once - Read - Many (WORM), and video / sound data on video cassettes, compact disks, and video disks.

Networking: If a system designed with the networking requirements in mind, the system hardware and software architectures can be optimally integrated with the networking interfaces and protocols.

4.7.5 Advantages of Client / Server model:

1. Client / Server technology will eliminate application backlogs, reduce software maintenance costs, increase application portability, improve systems and network performance.
2. Workstations deliver considerable computing power as like mainframe.
3. It is a special form of distributed processing - cooperative processing. Therefore Network traffic and response time can be greatly reduced, and effective throughput and carrying capacity on a heavily loaded network is increased. Conversely the network bandwidth requirements and therefore cost, can be reduced.
4. It facilitates the use of graphical user interfaces (GUI) available on powerful workstations.

4.7.6 Disadvantages of Client / Server model:

a) Server may become a bottleneck in the same fashion as a mainframe in a master - slave architecture.

b) Distributed applications, especially those designed for cooperative processing, are more complex than nondistributed.

c) There are certain claims made by various software vendors and an industry expert is that client / server will force minicomputers and mainframes to disappear.

4.8 Special techniques:

Any information system designer should be aware following special techniques, which can be used to improve the effectiveness of the system. He may pick and choose from these as required.

4.8.1Leased line: (Source: http://www.trah.com/leased-lines.htm)

This Series is ideal for full Internet connectivity for Local Area Networks (LANs) of all sizes, providing permanent access from 64k up to 2MB connections.

A Leased Line connection provides you with instant access to the Web and Email, thus eliminating the tedium of dial-up and login processes, and gives you permanently 'open' and unlimited access to the Internet. It will also provide you with fixed annual costs allowing you to budget correctly for your Internet and Email usage. Prices vary according to your companies' location and the capacity of the line required.

All Leased Lines have a **guaranteed 1:1 contention ratio** which means the bandwidth you pay is the bandwidth you get. All charges include Circuit Rental and Installation, Bandwidth Costs, IP Address Allocation, Domain Name Registrations and Mail Delivery.

In addition to the installed line you will require a Router, which support X.21 protocols. Support and supply of routers from Ascend Communications, Cisco Systems and Intel. A Bearer may also be required if fibre is used for the connection – this will be determined after a site survey. A number of different payment options on the lines and routers are available.

Technical information on leased line capacity

	64K	**128K**	**256K**	**512K**	**1MB**	**2MB**
Link Latency	60ms	30ms	20ms	10ms	7ms	4ms
Average throughput per 24 hours	550MB	1.1GB	2.2GB	4.4GB	8.8GB	17.6GB
Average Up-Time	99.85%	99.85%	99.85%	99.85%	99.85%	99.85%
Delivery method	X.21	X.21	X.21	X.21	X.21	G.703
24hr/365 day Fault Resolution	Yes	Yes	Yes	Yes	Yes	Yes

4.8.2 Smart card technology: (http://whatis.techtarget.com/definition/0,289893,sid9_gci213004,00.html)

A smart card is a plastic card about the size of a credit card, with an embedded microchip that can be loaded with data, used for telephone calling, electronic cash payments, and other applications, and then periodically refreshed for additional use. One can use a smart card to:

- Dial a connection on a mobile telephone and be charged on a per-call basis.
- Establish identity when logging on to an Internet access provider
- On line banking as customer

How Smart Cards Work

A smart card contains more information than a magnetic stripe card and it can be programmed for different applications. Some cards can contain programming and data to support multiple applications and some can be updated to add new applications after they are issued. Smart cards can be designed to be inserted into a slot and read by a special reader or to be read at a distance, such as at a toll booth. Cards can be disposable (as at a trade-show) or reloadable (for most applications).

An industry standard interface between programming and PC hardware in a smart card has been defined by the PC/SC Working Group, representing Microsoft, IBM, Bull, Schlumberger, and other interested companies.

4.8.3 Unicode technology:

Unicode(http://msdn.microsoft.com/library/default.asp?url=/library/enus/off2000/html/defUnicode.asp)

Definition:

A character-encoding scheme that uses two bytes to represent every character regardless of whether it's an ASCII character. This scheme is capable of encoding all known characters and is used as a worldwide character-encoding standard. Unicode is supported by all 32-bit versions of Microsoft Windows and by 32-bit OLE technology.

Unicode (http://register.consilium.eu.int/isoregister/help/htechEN.htm)

Technical Information

Multilingual requirements

In the UTF-8 version there are no restrictions: you can

select any language as your interface language and any language as your document language. The Welcome Page and the Information Page will check your environment (browser) and direct you automatically to the correct sub-environment (UTF-8). If for any reason this mechanism fails, you can go directly to the following addresses:

http://register.consilium.eu.int/utfregister.

Setting the character set

Your browser will automatically select the correct character-set encoding. If for any reason this mechanism fails, you can set it manually with the following commands:

Netscape 4.x: View, Character Set, Unicode (UTF-8);

IE 5.x : View, Encoding, Unicode (UTF-8);

IE 4.x : View, Fonts, Universal Alphabet (UTF-8);

Netscape 3.x : Options, Document Encoding:

Selecting fonts

To display all the languages correctly, you have to use an appropriate font. For Windows NT you should choose a Unicode Big font. This will display all characters correctly. Examples are Arial, Courier New, Lucida Console, Lucida Sans Unicode and Times New Roman.

Problems and suggested solutions

It should be noted that some problems were encountered during tests. Most of them were related to the multilingual aspect of the site. Where possible provisional solutions are suggested pending better multilingual support by the base technology.

Platform	Problem Encountered	Suggested Solutions
Microsoft IE 4.x	Navigating to different paragraphs on the same page is impossible when you are using UTF-8.	This is solved in IE 4.01 SP1

Platform	Problem Encountered	Suggested Solutions
Netscape 4.x	Searching on Greek characters does not work in UTF-8.	No solution.
	Sometimes the character set encoding as indicated in the HTML page does not switch the page automatically to UTF-8.	Reload the Page or Set the character set encoding manually to UTF-8 (View, Encoding, Unicode (UTF-8)).
Microsoft IE 4.x Netscape 4.x (under NT)	Greek characters are not printed correctly on UTF-8 pages.	You can print the HTML page using the option Print Text as Graphics. Select : File, Print ... , Properties, Advanced Tab, Print Text as Graphics in the Document Options.
Netscape 3.x	Searching on Greek characters does not work.	No solution.

4.8.4 Virtual Private Network technology: (http://mdnsweb1.mdns.att.com/att/att_tech_center4.html)

Technical Information

AT&T Virtual Private Network Service (VPNS) is a fully managed, remote dial and intranet / extranet access solution, with security options. It was designed for telecommuters, business travelers, and small branch offices that need access to LAN-based computing resources and intranet sites on the corporate network.

This section provides information about VPNS, including the following:

Service Components

- Nationwide Dial Access International Dial Access
- ISDN Access

- High-Speed Dedicated Connections via Frame Relay or Private Line

Security Features

- Authentication
- IP Closed User Groups
- Packet Filtering, Spoof Proofing, and Source Address Assurance
- Network-based Tunneling for Dial Access (Optional)
- Security for Dedicated Sites

Service Support

- AT&T Tier 2 Network Support
- AT&T Tier 1 End User Support (Optional)
- Network Monitoring

Optional Features

- Network Usage Reports
- Domain Name Service
- Client Software
- Network-based Tunneling for Dial Access (Optional)
- Proxy RADIUS Option
- Fully Managed Router Service

4.8.5 Middleware concepts

(Source: http://www.eecs.wsu.edu/~bakken/middleware-article-bakken.pdf)

Middleware is a class of software technologies designed to help manage the complexity and heterogeneity inherent in distributed systems. It is defined as a layer of software above the operating system but below the application program that provides a common programming abstraction across a distributed system. In doing so, it provides a higher-level building block for programmers than Application Programming Interfaces (APIs) such as sockets that are provided by the operating system. This significantly reduces the burden on application programmers by relieving them of this kind of tedious and error-prone programming. Middleware is sometimes informally called "plumbing" because it connects parts of a distributed application with data pipes and then passes data between them.

Middleware frameworks are designed to mask some of the kinds of heterogeneity that programmers of distributed systems must deal with. They always mask heterogeneity of networks and hardware. Most middleware frameworks also mask heterogeneity of operating systems or programming languages, or both. A few such as CORBA also mask heterogeneity among vendor implementations of the same middleware standard. Finally, programming abstractions offered by middleware can provide transparency with respect to distribution in one or more of the following dimensions: location, concurrency, replication, failures, and mobility.

e.g., IBM MQ Series, Web logic server, Tuxedo etc.

4.9 Interfacing techniques

It involves choice of server programs, and design of intermediate softwares, which process the information and make available at the client side. Choice of client side, is the ultimate.

APIs available for MySQL:

To facilitate application development, MySQL provides a client library written in the C programming language that allows you to access MySQL databases from within any C program. The client library implements an Application Programming Interface(API) that defines how client programs establish and carry out communication with the server. Client APIs exist for Perl, PHP, Java, Python, C++, Tcl and others.

1) *Interface between C and MySQL API:*

   This is the primary programming interface to MySQL.

   Hardware and Software Requirement:

   Linux operating system,

   Apache web server,

C compiler,

MySQL header file i.e., mysql.h,

Mysql client library i.e., libcgic.a

Compile and linking the client:

```
cc -c -I/usr/include/mysql $1.c
cc -o $1 $1.o -L/usr/lib/mysql -L./ -lmysqlclient -lcgic
```

2) *The DBI (Database Interface) API for the Perl general purpose scripting language:*

DBI is implemented as a Perl module that interfaces with other modules at the DBD (Database Driver) level, each of which provides access to a specific type of database engine.

Hardware and Software Requirement:

Linux operating system,

Apache web server,

Perl 5.0 software,

MySQL header file i.e., mysql.h,

Mysql client library i.e., libcgic.a

3) *The PHP API:*

PHP is a scripting language that provides a convenient way of embedding programs in web pages. Such a page is processed by PHP before being sent to the client, which allows the script to generate dynamic content, such as including the result of a MySQL query in the page. "PHP" meant Personal Home Page.

4) *Interface between C language and HTML:*

Hardware and Software Requirement:

Linux operating system,

Apache web server,

C compiler,

Browser like Netscape Navigator, Mozilla, etc,

CGI header file i.e., cgic.h,

Table 4.11 is helpful to select operating system with required web servers. Table 4.12 shows types of viruses and its required anti-virus choose from Table 4.13. Table 4.14 is helpful to select Security software to prevent from unauthorized user.

4.10 Some useful concept for System Manager:

To calculate the percent utilization:

Percent Utilization is defined as ratio of bits/hit (transmit + receive) and bandwidth (max capacity) required for total number of hits, i.e.,

Utilization / (max. capacity) = % utilization

Calculating Dynamic and Static content ratios:

When calculating the ratio of dynamic to static content served on a site, it is easy to overestimate. A good rule of thumb is that dynamic content is loaded from a database while static content loads from HTML, text or other static types of files.

Estimating number of hits:

Accurate sizing requires a good estimate of the average number of hits per day. The first approach presumes that you have access to web traffic information. In this case, calculate web traffic and break the day into four hour windows. Select the number of hits in the highest four - hour window. Multiply this figure by 6. Take the peak four hour period as your reference point and multiply it by 6 to determine hits per day. Once you have multiplied the number by 6, you can divide by 24 to determine hits per hour.

Each request is 650 bytes, the web server reply is 4000 bytes. (www.dell.com/us/en/topics/power-ps3q01-graham.htm). Then calculate network traffic rate for n hits.

Network traffic rate for number of requests per second i.e.,

Bandwidth(in bits/sec) = (client request in bytes + web server response in bytes) * (requests/sec)

= (650 + 4000) * n bytes/sec

= (4650) * n * 8 bits/sec.

4.11 Difference between a portal and a corporate web site:

(Ref: http://www.fastwebsites.co.uk/portvscorp.htm)

A portal and a corporate web site are two separate entities, complementing each other. They need to be strongly linked together, but they should not replace each other.

A corporate site presents an organization to the outside world. It has to be centered on the organization's products and services that it is trying to promote to all existing and potential customers.

A portal is aimed at a specific market sector. The members of this community need to find on the portal all topics that interest them and can have an impact on their business, so that they keep on visiting day after day.

Therefore, a business portal needs to cover a much wider range of topics than a corporate web site. It also needs to be updated daily, and should provide a wide range of interactive services and forums where industry members can discuss and express their views.

To use a comparison from the printed media, a corporate web site is to some extent an online corporate brochure, while an industry portal is aimed at the companies operating in the industry and their suppliers, with a wide range of professional services and business resources. An industry portal is therefore similar to a reference library, a trade magazine, the daily press and the business Yellow Pages all rolled into one.

We can link our industry portals to the corporate web sites of our partners and other selected companies, which will drive increased traffic on their web sites, increase their customers' satisfaction and create additional opportunities to promote their organization and their products or services.

Chapter 5
Farm - Advisory Subsystem

5.0 Introduction

Crop production technology is improved by constant experimentation and research-by-research workers in various research institutions even progressive farmers add to technology by constant experimentation. The Agricultural Extension worker takes this information to farmers and brings back their views and experience in the form of feedback. This feedback helps the research worker in improving the technology further. This is a continuous process of development. This depends on the linkage among farmer, EP and researcher. This is exactly what is a Farm - advisory subsystem. Presently such a system is in existence in the form of T&V system (Ch.2 and Ch. 3). It is necessary to transform the existing system into a modern electronic based farm advisory subsystem, as has been already emphasized in earlier chapters. We will now discuss how a IT based farm-advisory system should be. It is essentially a Farmer - Extension worker - Research worker linkage.

A good farm advisory should have the following attributes:

Farmer should have:

- easy access to information
- convenient facilities to post queries
- to post his views from any where.

Extension worker should have facilities to:

- Answer /Respond to queries
- update information sitting in their offices
- or on the move from where.

Researchers should :

- continuously get feedbacks

- be able to update information from his office
- or on the move from anywhere

On the information side:

- The system should be made intelligent enough to be automatically added to the banks.
- Bilingual communication should be possible.

5.1 Suggested models

Experienced farmers, NGO's, crop specialist, disease and pest specialist etc if they choose can run advisory systems based on Design specification 1 and 2 (chapter 4) for advising their clientele.

State department of agriculture which are currently running T&V system may think of going for an advisory system based on Design specification 4 or 5 to strengthen the current system. The design aspects of advisory systems based on Design specification 4 or 5 are discussed in this chapter.

5.2 Information content

We have already identified components of information contents of different models in Chapter 4. We will not discuss again how advisory systems based on Design specification 1 and 2 should be designed in respect of contents. Design specification 4 and 5, which are recommended for large organizations like SDA may require more specific identification with regards to contents design. Hence they are discussed here.

- They should contain the following static pages:
    1. Newsletter (weekly or bi-weekly),
    2. Scientific / extension journal (quarterly or half yearly),
    3. Information regarding seed and fertilizer dealers,
    4. Loans and subsidi schemes,
    5. Annual reports (corporate) ,
    6. List of experts and links to them,
    7. Links to other important sites,
    8. Adequate number of FAQs,

9. Adequate number of HowTos,

- and following dynamic facilities:
  1. Membership registration,
  2. Form processing tools,
  3. Mail service for members,
  4. Chat sessions,
  5. Video conferencing facilities,
  6. Expert systems,
  7. Operation research tools,
  8. Maps and tools for analysis (GIS).

Now we will discuss a few of the important components:

5.3 Description of components of static information:

Apart from the fact that Newsletters and Scientific journals will be in the electronic form and will be available to the user at a click of mouse, there structure will be same as their counterparts in the printed form.

Frequently asked questions (FAQ) and HowTos are electronic documents generally indexed and provisions of links to help quick electronic search. Frequent up-gradations and ease of search are two attributes required. FAQs and HowTos should be on package of practices, selection of varieties and so on.

Static pages about seed , fertilizers, loan and subsidy should make addresses of dealers, manufacturers, agencies for loans available to the farmer at the click of a mouse. Conditions for loans, rules for subsidies if provided will help the user remain sleep.

One of the major objectives of advisory system is direct contact between the experts and the users. A quick access to an expert and communication to the expert will solve large number of the problems of the user effectively. Hence any advisory system should provide the list of experts and links to their E-mail addresses. A key to the specialization of the expert is a must.

Providing links to other similar sites is also very important because no advisory system can be complete itself. This will guide the user in acquiring more information whenever needed.

5.4 Description of components of dynamic pages

Registration to the advisory system should be a necessity. This should be done through an interactive form-processing tool, which should culminate into allocation of a unique identification number to the user. The user should be encouraged to contact the advisory system always with his unique id. This will also help in formulating forums of common interest later.

There are many situations where interactive form processing tools can help in advisory. One commonly used facility could be sending the soil testing report to the farmer after he submits soil sample for testing at the laboratory. We assume to start with that soil-testing laboratory is a node on the advisory network. The whole process of how this can be done is given below.

Assume that soil scientists have a PC at his office. Farmer clicks to 'Form button' on the portal. Then it will display list of forms available on the PC. Then click to 'Soil testing form', figure 5.7 shows which entries should fill by farmer and soil sample given by the farmer. After submitting the form, the system will generate a token id and farmer will obtain report at his place by logging on to Internet on soil scientists portal, giving token id to the system and obtaining the report.

Similarly, loan-processing facilities, subsidy facilities can be atomized through form processing tools provided in the advisory system.

Without E-mail services and chat services, no IT enabled advisory system can be complete. Communication among farmers is also equally important as communication between experts and farmers. This helps in proper dissemination of information.

Figure 5.8 is given detail procedure of how on-line or instant chat established with extension expert.

Video conferencing tool is useful in case of visual chat with

कृषी खाते, महाराष्ट्र राज्य, पुणे

(मातीच्या नमुन्यासोयत खालील माहिति पाठवावी)

नमुन्याचा माहिती तक्ता

१. नमुना क्रमांक ...

२. नमुना घेतल्याची तारीख ...

३. शेतकवाचे संपूर्ण नाव ...

४. शेतकरी मागासंवर्गीय आहे काय?
असल्यास पोटजात ...

५. गांव ... पोष्ट

६. तालुका ...

७. जिल्हा ...

८. सर्व्हे नं. किंवा ठिकाण ...

९. जमिनीचा उतार ...

१०. पाण्याचा निचरा ...

११. काही विशेष लक्षणे ...

१२. जमिनीची खोली ...

१३. पुढील पीक (जात) ...

१४. ओलित-कोरडवाहू ...

१५. नमुना घेतलेल्या जमिनीचे प्राति
निधीक क्षेत्र ...

नमुना घेणाराची सही.

Figure 5.7 : Specimen of Soil Testing form.

experts and also in case of providing training to extension worker, arranging seminars or workshops or conferences.

Expert systems for specific crops like cotton growing, grape growing, seed productions that are highly skilled production systems may be made available on the advisory system for ready use of the growers. This will reduce lot of repetitive work which the experts may have to perform.

Expert systems are interactive (Waterman (1986)). They are based on knowledge base created by highly skilled people; hence their knowledge becomes automatically sharable. An example of the Expert System - Building Process of cotton crop. The following steps are to be followed while designing an Expert system.

- *Characterizing the problem:* Identification, where the task is to identify participants, resources, goals and problem characteristics.
- *What concepts are needed to produce a solution:* Knowledge Engineer who designs an Expert system entering into the next phase i.e., conceptualization. Here he makes the explicit key concepts and relations needed to solve problems in the domain. This domain includes project goal, main problem, subproblems, problem characteristics, data, important concepts and solution.
- *How can the knowledge be formally represented:* Next step is the formulation, where the key concepts, subproblems and control features are mapped into a more formal representation suggested by an Expert system building tool.
- *Implementing a prototype system:* Knowledge Engineer now enters into the implementation phase in which he turns the concepts and relations between them into a working computer program.
- *Validating the rules:* He enters into the testing phase. He attempts to validate the rules that have been formulated. In a more fully developed system he run the program on a few cases and ask how well it predicted the value or solution.

Operation Research tools if properly used can help in optimum solutions i.e., profit maximization solutions regarding cropping patterns, cropping systems, resource allocations to the farmer which will help in making cost effective business.

Objective function would be the profit and constraints would be the resources available with the farmer. On supply of information by the farmer through an interactive form, the program based on O.R. tools should give him advise regarding cropping pattern, cropping systems to be adopted.

Specimen of GIS map shown in Map 5. GIS software is

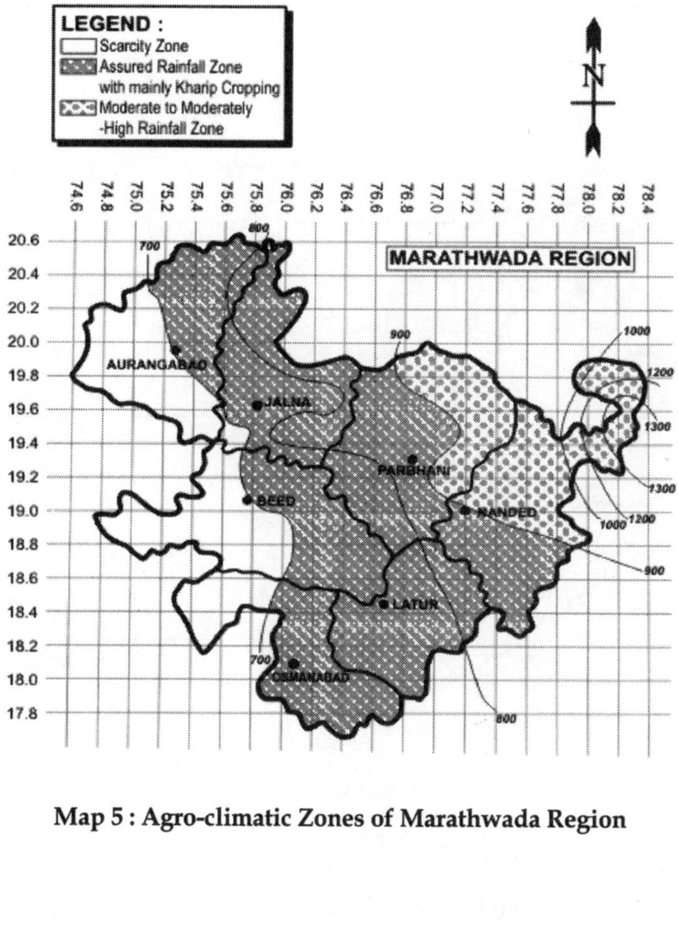

Map 5 : Agro-climatic Zones of Marathwada Region

useful in case of mapping analysis. In case of Farm - Advisory system, the following maps should be available:

- Map to show area in cereals, pulses, oilseeds, grain, cash crops, fruits and vegetables in Marathwada region.
- Map to show soil type, its classification, relationship and coverage of area in Marathwada region.
- Map to show crop type, area in hectare and production per hectare in Marathwada region.
- Map to show rainfall pattern of every district in Marathwada region.

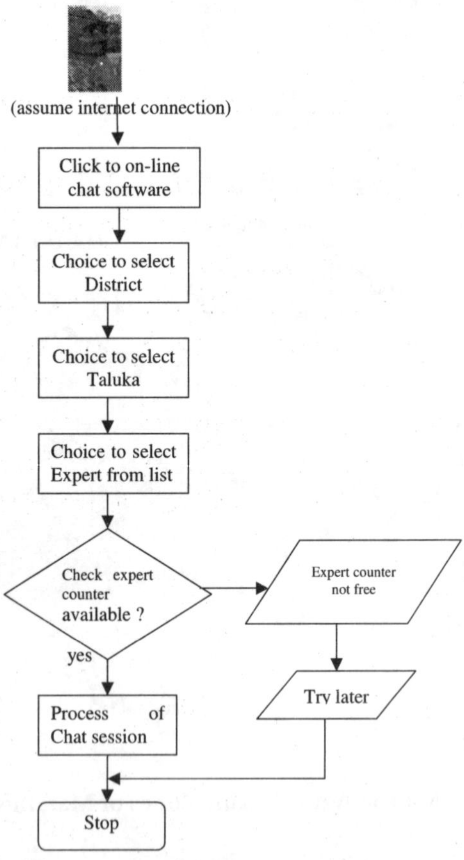

Figure 5.8: on-line or instant chat with Extension expert:

5.5 A prototype of Self Upgrading Advisory Tool For Extension.

As an illustrative implementation, A Self Upgrading Agricultural Advisory Tool has been developed and tested as a part of this study. It has a very strong farmer-extension worker interactive mode. Its knowledge base keeps growing making the tool more and more effective at it grows old. To begin with we describe its architecture.

MySql is used as the supporting Relational database Management System (RDBMS) . CGI-Scripts written in perl, C and C++. Its first launch was on the URL http://mkv2.mah.nic.in/adv/main.html . Apache is used as the webserver. At user end Netscape Navigator or Internet explorer or any equivalent browser is adequate. We have tested the tool using both Netscape Navigator (version 4.2) and Internet Explorer 4.0 onwards. Currently Agra font is used for Marathi communication.

The server (mkv2.mah.nic.in)ran on Linux RedHat 7.2. The software choice fell on open source products because we could procure them without worrying much about copyright violations. The INTRANET facility at Marathwada Agricultural University (MAU) was used to rest run the tool. Demonstrations were also arranged at the Directorate of Extension of MAU and Agricultural Information Technology Cell of MAU to gauge the opinions of experts. Sample of source code is given in Appendix 1.

The first page, apart from other information has provision to accept login, password, of user. A user may belong to any of the following groups:

Farmer or information seeker - (he may only query and receive replies)

Extension officer - (he has permission to update information)

Administrator - (he can supervise the process)

Interactive provisions provided in the tool:

Farmer - System Interaction :

- Connect to the cyber cafe.
- Direct access to static information.
- Login if you want a query.
- Submit a query.
- Answer will be flashed if available.
- Otherwise question put in a queue.
- Answer flashed at the subsequent login.

Extension Worker - System interaction :

- Connect from anywhere on the Lan.
- Log on to the system using password.
- Pending queries will be visible.
- Provide answers.

Administrator - System interaction :

- Connect to the Server.
- Maintain the system.
- Examine user statistics.
- Troubleshooting if any.

Bi-lingual communication:

- Marathi and English query sessions are parellely possible.

Relational Database Management System (RDBMS):

This system consists of two databases named as adv_english and adv_marathi. Adv_english is specially designed for English query processing and adv_marathi is used for marathi query processing. Layout is shown in Fig 5.6.

Table structures of both the databases are identical. Structures of each table are described below.

Data structure of ans_table:

Every question has a unique question identification number (qid). The structure of the ans_table is given in Table 5.2.

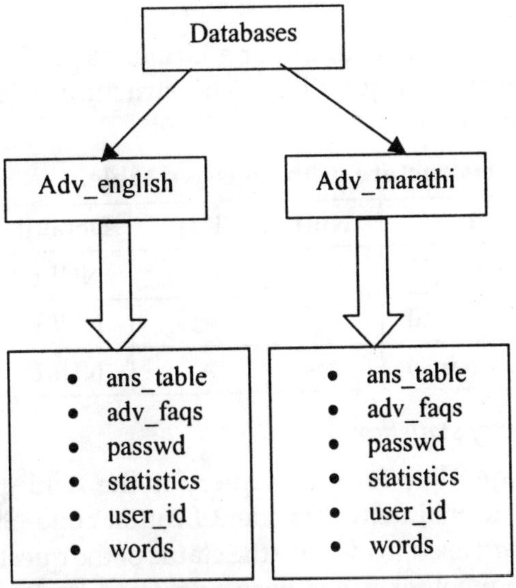

Figure 5.6: Layout structure of database

Table 5.2: Structure of the ans_table.

Field	Type	Null	Key	Default	Extra
Qid	Int(5)	Yes		NULL	
Que	Blob	Yes		NULL	

Data structure of adv_faqs:

Field name qid indicates question identification number, which is uniquely maintained in required or interrelated tables. This adv_faqs table is specially designed in order to maintain all question and answer database. The structure of the dv_faqs table is given in 5.3.

Table 5.3: The structure of the adv_faqs table.

Field	Type	Null	Key	Default	Extra
Question	Blob	Yes		NULL	
Answer	Blob	Yes		NULL	
Qid	Int(6)	Yes		NULL	

Data structure of passwd:

The field user_type = 'E' identifies and extension officer,

for administrator, user_type = 'A'.

No password is required for a farmer or general user who is only interested in querying . The structure of the passwd table is given in 5.4.

Table 5.4: The structure of the passwd table.

Field	Type	Null	Key	Default	Extra
Password	Char(10)	Yes		NULL	
Userid	Char(10)	Yes		NULL	
User_type	Char(1)	Yes		NULL	

Data structure of statistics:

The unique key for every query is the field qid. Userid field is used to maintain user identification code. Status1 and status2 field are used to identify the status of the question posted in respect of whether it has been answered by the extension officer and to count how many queries are still pending unsolved. Qdate is the field which is used to store the date of posting of query and ansdate denotes on which date query is solved. The structure of the statistics table is given in 5.5.

Table 5.5: The structure of the statistics table.

Field	Type	Null	Key	Default	Extra
Qid	Int(5)		Pri	0	
Userid	Char(10)	Yes		NULL	
Status1	Char(1)	Yes		NULL	
Status2	Char(1)	Yes		NULL	
Qdate	Date	Yes		NULL	
Ansdate	Date	Yes		NULL	

Data structure of user_id:

This table maintain a statistics of how many user created from the universe. The structure of the user_id table is given in Table 5.6.

Table 5.6: The structure of the user_id table.

Field	Type	Null	Key	Default	Extra
First	Char(25)	Yes		NULL	
Middle	Char(25)	Yes		NULL	
Last	Char(25)	Yes		NULL	
Village	Char(25)	Yes		NULL	
Taluka	Char(25)	Yes		NULL	
userid	Char(6)	Yes		NULL	

Data structure of words:

This table specially designed to store basic words. The structure of the words table is given in 5.7. These words are important in searching for the answers.

Table 5.7: The structure of the words table.

Field	Type	Null	Key	Default	Extra
Strings	Varchar(50)	Yes		NULL	

Decision Table of Farm advisory subsystem is given in table 5.1.

Table 5.1: Decision Table of Extension Information Subsystem

Activity		Decision Rules					
		Rule 1	Rule 2	Rule 3	Rule 4	Rule 5	Rule 6
CONDITION	If login as user / farmer	Y	Y	N	N	N	N
	If login as Extension officer	N	N	Y	Y	N	N
	If login as Administrator	N	N	N	N	Y	Y
	If query is in English	Y	N	Y	N	Y	N
	If query is in Marathi	N	Y	N	Y	N	Y
ACTION	Ask query in English	Y					
	Ask query in Marathi		Y				
	Solve questions in English			Y			
	Solve questions in Marathi				Y		
	Display statistics of English database					Y	
	Display statistics of Marathi database						Y

Figure 5.1-5.5 depict the, Data flow diagram of Question - Answer session, the System flowchart of Farmer - System Interface, System flowchart of Extension Officer - System Interface, Farmer - System Interface with a DFD, Extension Officer - System Interface with a DFD respectively.

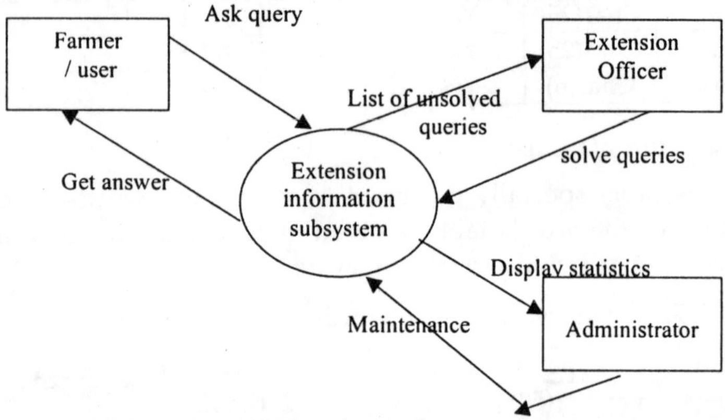

Figure 5.1: Data flow diagram of Question – Answer system

Pseudo code for the process of Farmer - System Interface:

- Click on one of the browser.
- Give the address of the web site.
- Login as an farmer with id.
- Click on the query option.
- It will give choice to enter question either in Marathi or English.
- It will display the table of previously asked questions,

that may be solved or   Provision to post question (2)   Back to the main page (3)

unsolved question - answer

links are provided.

And back to main page(1)

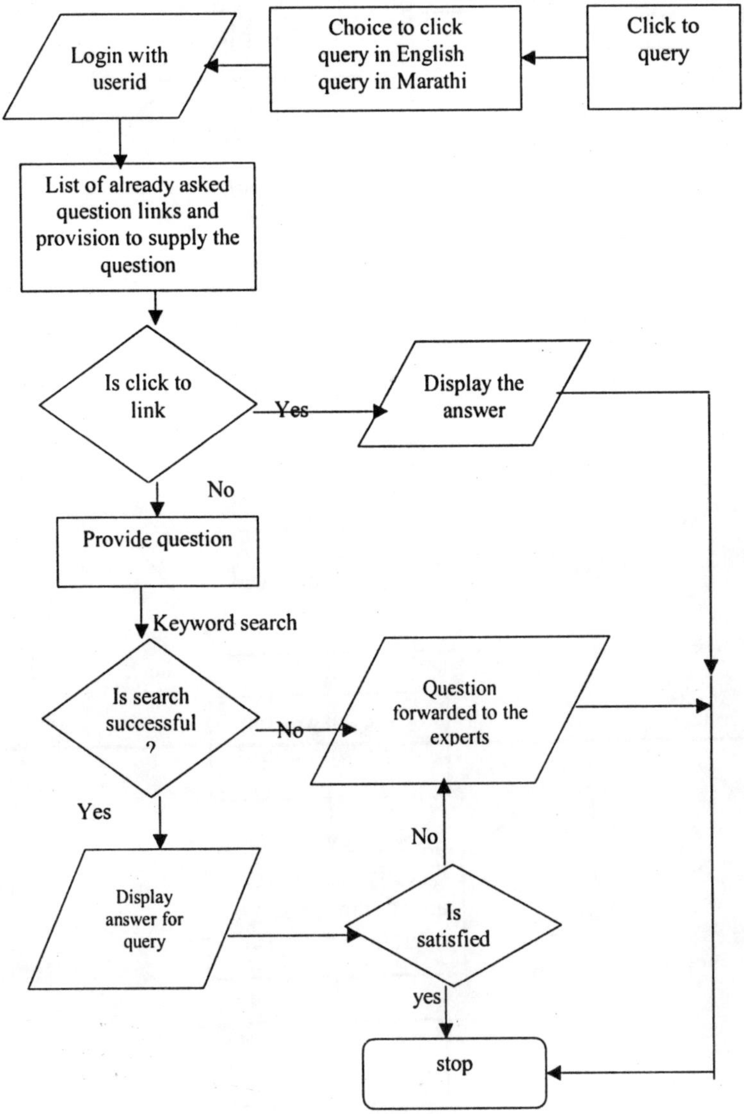

Figure 5.2: System flowchart of Farmer - System Interface

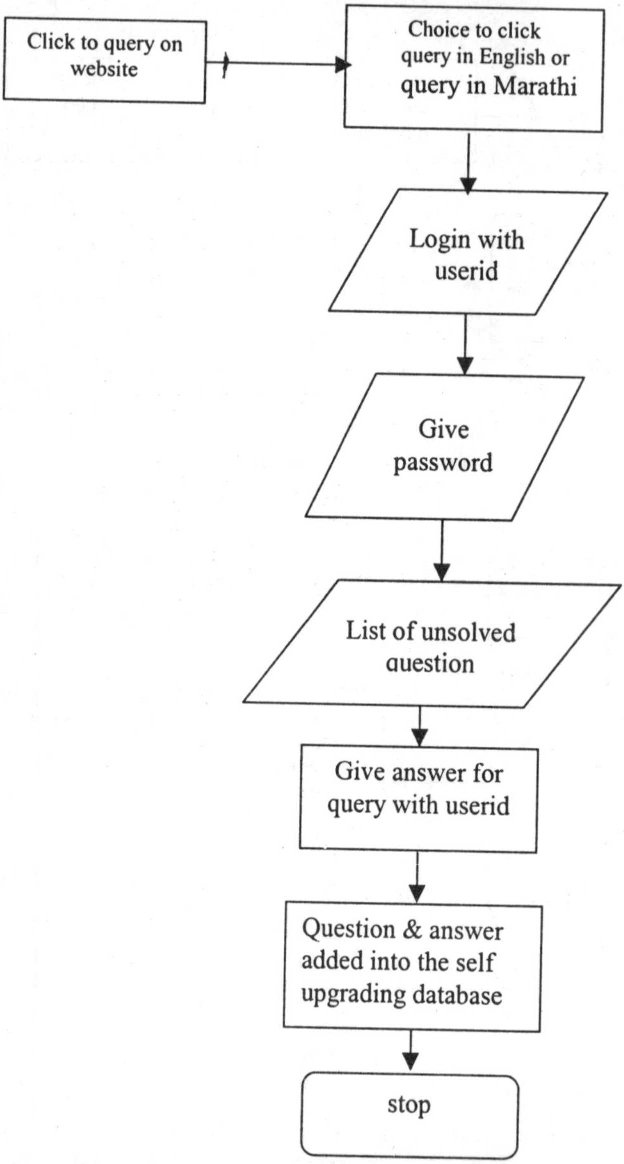

Figure 5.3: System flowchart of Extension Officer - System Interface:

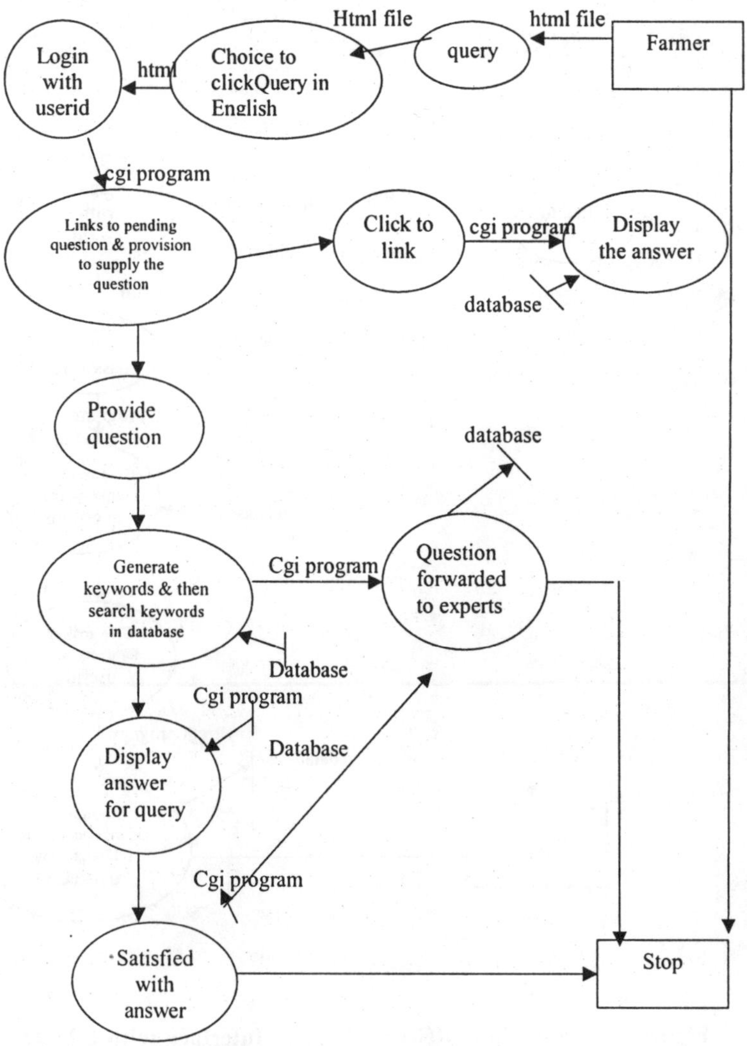

Figure 5.4: Farmer - System Interface with a DFD:

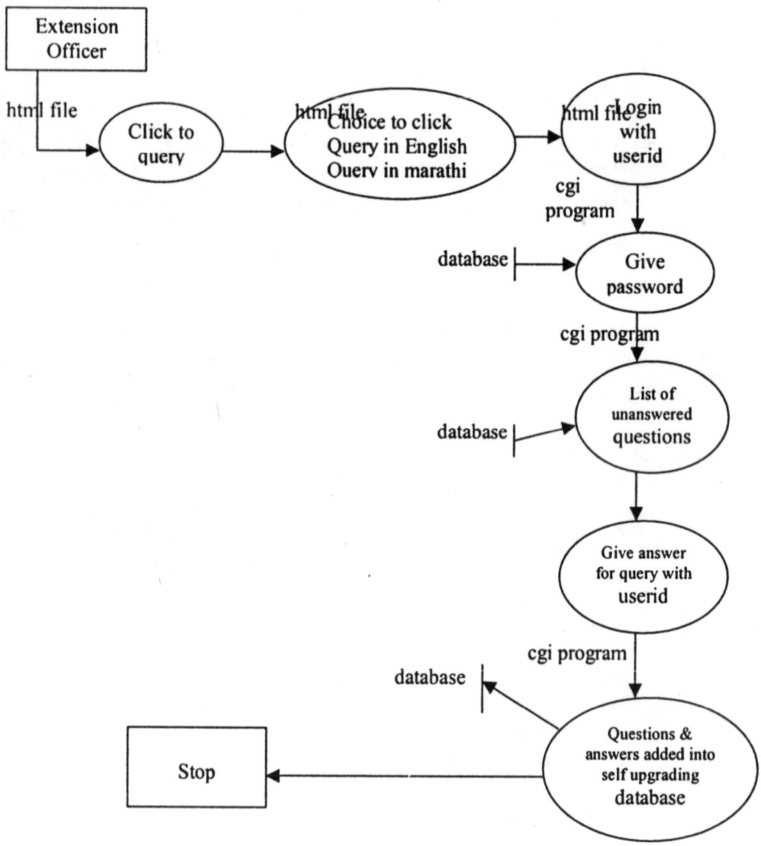

Figure 5.5: Extension Officer - System Interface with a DFD

Choose one of the alternative.

- (2) It will display the possible answer if available in the question - answer bank and ask the user, are you satisfied with given answer, if yes then no problem otherwise question forwarded to the experts data bank.
- Back to the main page.

Pseudo code for the process of Extension worker -system Interface:

- Click on one of the browser.
- Give the address of the web site.
- Login as an Extension worker with id.
- Click on the query option.
- It will give choice to solve questions from either in Marathi or English data bank.
- It will display the list of unsolved questions with unique id number.
- Provision to give id number of question which is solved by expert.
- Provision to post answer for the selected question.
- Solved question and answer shifted into the question - answer bank.
- Back to the main page.

Pseudo code for the process of Administrator - System Interface:

- Click on one of the browser.
- Give the address of the web site.
- Login as an Administrator with id.
- Click on the query option.
- Choice to see statistics of Marathi question - answer data bank or English question - answer data bank.
- It will display the statistics regarding how many questions solved by electronic system, solved by extension worker and questions still unsolved.
- Back to the main page.

5.6 Icon based query formation tool or Search Engine with keyword search:

Data flow diagram of query formation tool or search engine is given in figure 5.9. The following steps are required in icon based keyword search:

1. Login on to the system,
2. Choose icon based primary keyword from Table 5.9,
3. Choose icon based secondary keyword from Table 5.10, if needed repeat step 2,
4. Choose information generator keyword from Table 5.11, if needed repeat step 2,
5. Choose choice level

   1 for 75 % possible solutions,

   2 for 60 % possible solutions,

   3 for 50 % possible solutions.
6. Display links of possible solution, otherwise no solution, go to step 8.
7. Click to required link for query satisfaction.
8. End of search.

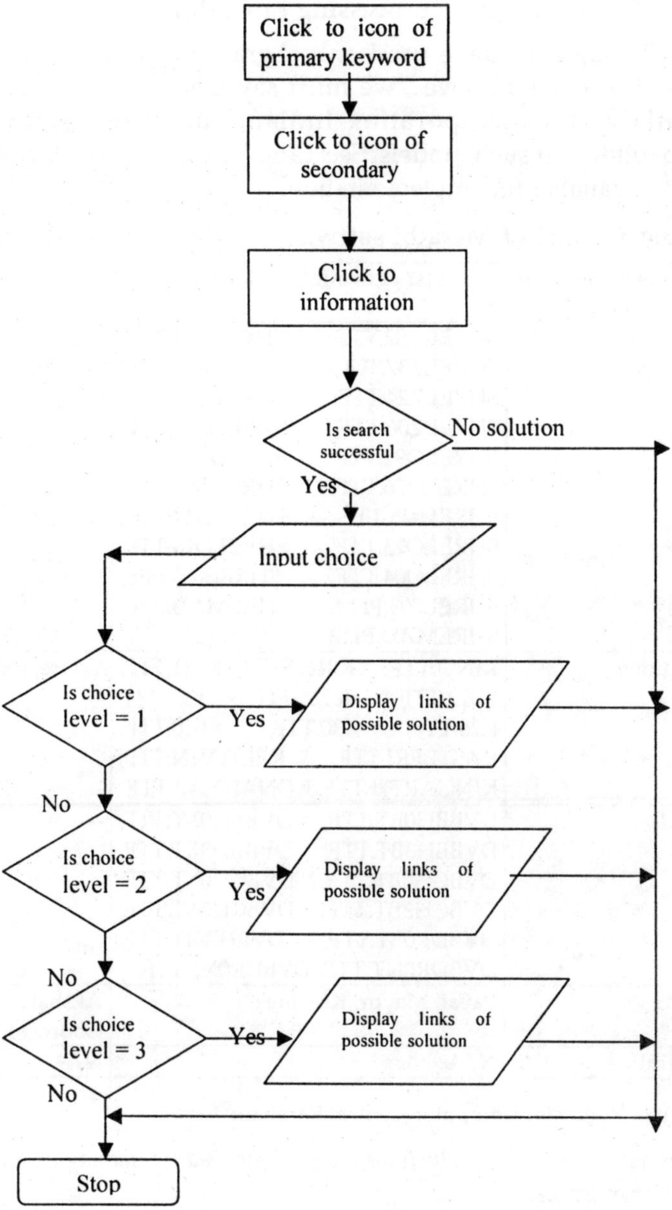

Figure 5.9: Data flow diagram of icon based query formation tool or search engine:

5.7 Indian language processing capabilities

Though we have used only Agra font in our prototype model discussed above , we must say that many options are available for incorporating Indian Language Processing Capabilities in such models. See Table5.8 for a list of Devnagari fonts available for implementation.

Table 5.8: List of Marathi software's and its fonts:

Name of Marathi software	List of available Marathi fonts	Keyboard type
Shrilipi	SHRELA92.TTF, SHRELZ44.TTF, SHRELZ37.TTF, SHRELZ33.TTF, SHRELZ24.TTF, SHRELZ19.TTF, SHRELZ06.TTF, SHRELO94.TTF, SHRELO92.TTF, SHRELO80.TTF, SHRELO76.TTF, SHRELO52.TTF, SHREL045.TTF, SHRELO40.TTF, SHRELO23.TTF, SHRELO18.TTF, SHRELO04.TTF, SHREL703.PFB, SHREL703.PFM, SHREM703.PFB, SHREM703.PFM	Remington, Akruti, Godrej etc
Kritidev	KINO.TTF, K016.TTF, K021.TTF, K022.TTF, K024.TTF, K25.TTF K26.TTF, K30.TTF, K010.TTF, KASTLERI.TTF, KELTONN.TTF, KINGARTH.TTF, KONANKAP.TTF	Godrej only
ISM	DVBBH0BT.TTF, DVBBH0XT.TTF, DVBBH3BT.TTF, DVBBH3XT.TTF, DVBCH0BT.TTF, DVBCH0XT.TTF, DVBCH3BT.TTF, DVBCH3XT.TTF, DVBDR0BT.TTF, DVBDR0IT.TTF, DVBDR0NT.TTF, DVBDR0XT.TTF	--
APS	Payal, Mayur, Krishna etc	Akshar, Godrej etc
Sulipi	N/A	N/A

Source: Pratiksha Computer Centre, Parbhani

Here is the procedure which we adopted for loading devnagari font on the linux server.

(How to configure True Type Marathi fonts on linux)

1) CD /usr/X11R6/lib/X11/fonts

Table 5.9. Primary keyword

हवामान	जमीन	खत	पीक	पाणी
मृद	अवजारे	जनावरे	श्रोग	..
बी-बीयाणे	दळणवळण			
रोगनाशक	किटकनाशक	बुरशीनाशक		

Table 5.10. Secondary keyword

हवामान	जमीन	खत	पीक	पाणी	अवजारे	रोग
पर्जन्य	खनिज	नत्र	साळ	पाऊस	फावड़ा	सड
मान	कोरडवाहू	स्फुरद	बाजरी	कालवा	सुरपी	मर
तपमान	ओलित	पालाश	मटकी	प्रकल्प	गिरमीट	करपा
		शेणखत	तुर	नदी		गोसा
		कंपोस्ट	मुग	नाले		वी
		सेंद्रिय	हरभरा	बांध		
		रासायनिक	सुर्यफल	विहिर		
		लेंडी खत	करडई	शेततळे		
		पेंडी	कापूस	गावतळे		
		मासळी		पाझर		
		जिवाणू		तलावा		
		शिंग खत				
मृद	जनावरे	रोग नाशक	किटक नाशक	बि-बियाड़े	दळण-वळण	
..		..		..	..	

Table 5.11. Information generator keyword

प्रमाण	पोत	घनता	उपलब्ध	जल
हलक्या	मध्यम	भारी	संकरित	प्रदेश
नंतर	क्षेत्र	हेक्टर	निचरा	वाढ
उगवण	क्षार	तपासणी	मात्रा	भुसा
शेत	-हास	मळी	साठा	अन्नद्रव्य
रंग	सुपीकता	नांगरणी	कापणी	पूर्वी
खोली	उतार	वाण	पेरणी	फवारणी
क्रिया	निष्कर्ष	टाकाऊ	सुधारित	पर्यंत
तंत्र	सुपिकता	पाणलोट	धुप	पद्धत
निवड	विरळणी	मशागत	भेसळ	उत्पादन
क्षार				

2) Mkdir TrueType
3) Cd Truetype
4) Cp *.ttf /usr/X11R6/lib/X11/fonts/TrueType
5) Ttmkfdir -o fonts.scale
6) Mkfontdir
7) Joe /etc/X11/fs/conf
8) If path not present, then add line at the end of path list, /usr/X11R6/lib/X11/fonts/TrueTyne
9) save and exit
10) execute command: /etc/rc.d/init.d/xfs restart

Download agra font :

http://user.dtcc.edu/~berlin/font/indian.htm

TrueType fonts: *http://whatis.techtarget.com/definition/0,,sid9_gci214629,00.html*

Created at Apple Computer, TrueType was designed to fill the need for an optimized, scalable font format. The format uses *hinting,* a technique that preserves a font's design, even at a small scale or on a display with low resolution. It was initially developed in response to the technical limitations of Adobe's Postscript and Type 1 font formats.

TrueType was first introduced in the Macintosh System 7 operating system in 1990. A year later, Apple licensed TrueType to Microsoft, and it was introduced in their Windows 3.1 operating system. After making some performance improvements to the format, they released version 1.5 in Windows NT 3.1, and have continued to update the format.

In order to view and print TrueType fonts on a computer, two components are necessary: the actual TrueType font file (with the extension TTF) and the TrueType raster graphics. The rasterizer is built into Windows and Mac operating systems.

If you use TrueType fonts on a Web page or in Word document, it is possible to embed them into the file, so that your fonts will still be viewable by people who do not have that font installed on their machine. Also keep in mind that the

Macintosh and Windows versions of TrueType fonts are not compatible. When downloading TrueType fonts from the Internet (such as from a free fonts Web site), you must select the Mac or PC version. TrueType Font converters are available if a TrueType font is only available for one platform.

Microsoft's most recent font development is called OpenType. This font format ensures that fonts are compatible across the Windows and Apple Macintosh platforms and encompasses Adobe's Type 1 and PostScript technologies.

Multilingual requirements are discussed in 4.8.3.

5.8 Voice Recognition Software

(Source: http://www.worc.ac.uk/services/equalopps/VRproject/voicerec.htm)

Voice Recognition (VR) programmes will soon become essential if one can provide voice data transfer through these advisory systems. Currently the technology does not seem to have standardized itself for convenient use. Hence we have not considered this aspect of communication and we have not attempted to incorporate it in our prototype.

Chapter 6

Agricultural Marketing Subsystem

6.0 Introduction:

Chandel C.G. (1980) has mentioned that Agricultural marketing involves buying and selling of agricultural produce. In modern marketing, important marketing functions are a) assembling (concentration), b) preparation for consumption (processing) and c) distribution (dispersion). At the market, the produce may be sold by the farmer direct to the consumer or through a commission agent.

A 'Market Committee' consisting of the representatives of growers, traders, merchants, local bodies and government nominees, administers the working of each market. The functions of the market committee are to frame bye-laws, define local market practices, fix market charges payable to various functionaries, license the functionaries, settle disputes, supervise weightment and promote the development of 'orderly marketing' in general.

It is necessary to transform into the modern electronic-based Agricultural Marketing subsystem. We will now discuss how a IT based Agricultural marketing system should be.

A good agricultural market should have the attributes like:

- To access arrivals, sales and prices of every commodity from every market, upgraded everyday.
- Online facilities like license holder registration, renewal etc.
- Information on roads, distances, transportation.
- Table of financial fee or renewal fee.
- Market rate predictions / demand predictions / stability

analysis.

- Tools of market analysis and
- Expert system and AI tools.

Bilingual communication should be possible.

6.1 Agriculture Market website:

Information on Regulated market are currently available on the following sites:

- http://www.marketonline.com (This Domain is for sale)
- http://www.ams.usda.gov (Agricultural Marketing Service)
- http://www.agmrc.org (A National Information Resource for Value-added Agriculture)
- http://www.nama.org (National Agri-Marketing Association)
- http://www.statpub.com (Market Intelligence for the World's Agriculture Industry)
- http://www.agriculture.com (Agriculture Online)
- http://www.aec.msu.edu/agecon/fs2/market_information.htm (Market Information Sources available Through the Internet: Dailyto Yearly Market and Outlook Reports, Prices, Commodities and Quote)
- http://www.agrimark.com (Agri. Marketing for online information management systems)

In most cases, the information available is just rates, arrivals of goods, etc but information specific to particular region, particular market is not available on the sites which is the need of the current day.

6.2 Suggested models

Different models of marketing information systems would be recommendable for different marketing channels (fig 6.1)

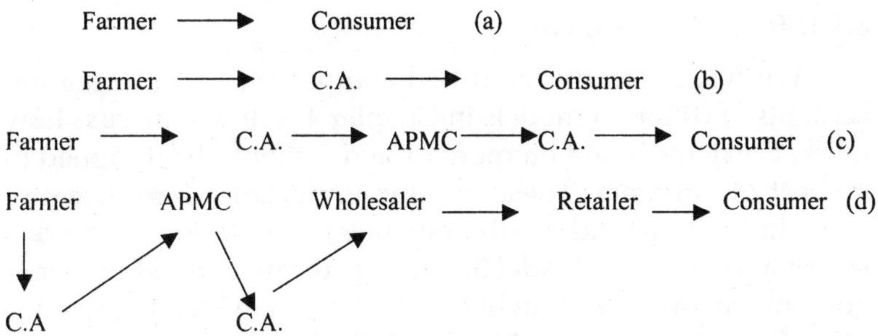

Figure 6.1: Different channels of Agricultural Marketing

Experienced farmers, commission agents if they choose can run marketing systems based on Models 1 and 2 (Chapter 4) for advising their clientele, and to provide e-marketing facilities.

APMC who are currently running Agricultural grain and cotton market system may think of going for an Agricultural Market system based on Model 3 to strengthen the current system. The design aspects of Agricultural Market systems based on model 4 is discussed in this chapter.

Fig 6.2 illustrate client - server architecture of controlled marketing system. All SMC PCs connected to the Internet server of MMC and helpful to obtain static and dynamic pages from server. Static and dynamic web page information details are mentioned in 6.3.

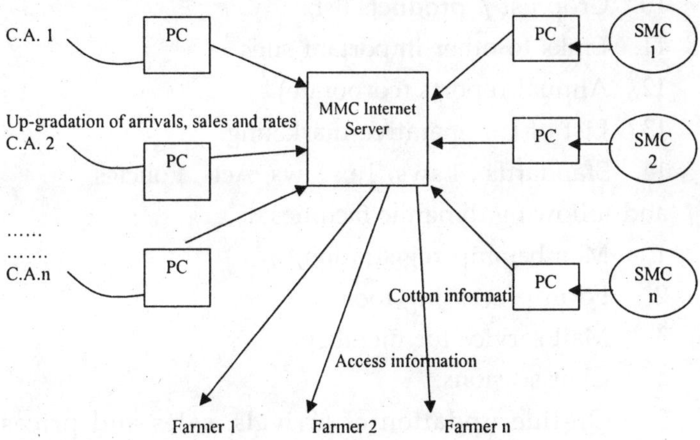

Figure 6.2: Client - Server architecture of controlled marketing system.

6.3 Information content

We have already identified components of information contents of different models in Chapter 4. We will discuss how market systems based on model 1 and 2 should be designed in respect of contents. These assume importance here because many individuals and small companies to host their own market information system. Model 3, which is recommended for semi-government organizations like APMC may require more specific identification with regard to content's design. Hence they are discussed here.

- They should contain following static pages:
  1. Newsletter (weekly or bi-weekly),
  2. Adequate number of FAQs,
  3. Adequate number of HowTos,
  4. List of commission agents and their addresses,
  5. List of license holder,
  6. Storage facility,
  7. Godown facility,
  8. Auction procedure,
  9. Latest information about sales and prices of various markets,
  10. Crop list / products list,
  11. Links to other important sites,
  12. Annual reports (corporate) ,
  13. List of Co-operative marketing,
  14. Standards , Laws, Tax laws, Acts, Policies.
- and following dynamic facilities:
  1. Membership registration,
  2. Form processing tools,
  3. Mail service for members,
  4. Chat sessions,
  5. On-line updation of arrivals, sales and prices of various commodities from various markets,

6. Operation research tools,
7. Transportation cost calculation tool,
8. Import facility,
9. Export facility,
10. Market analysis,
11. Maps and tools for analysis (GIS).

Now we will discuss few of the important components.

6.4 Description of components of static information

Apart from the fact that Newsletters will be in the electronic form and will be available to the user at a click of mouse, their structure will be same as their counterparts in the printed form.

Frequently asked questions (FAQ) and HowTos are electronic documents generally indexed and provisions of links to help quick electronic search. FAQs and HowTos should be on arrivals and prices of various commodities, membership regarding license and renewal, selection of market for high profit, queries from farmer and so on.

Static pages about List of commission agents and their addresses, list of license holder should be maintained for further correspondence.

Storage, cooling and godown facilities are needed for various types of commodities, and which is available in the market or not is displayed on web page for user.

Auction procedure is needed for new license holders or wholesalers or retailers at the initial stage.

Updated sales and prices of various commodities of various markets should be displayed on the page; by which the farmer can take decision about where to sell the grain or cotton with maximum profit and less transportation cost.

Crop list of every market should be provided, by which farmer can take decision where to sell the goods.

Providing links to other similar sites is also very important because no Agricultural market system can be complete in itself.

This will guide the user in acquiring more information whenever needed.

6.5 Description of components of dynamic pages

Registration to the Agricultural Market system should be a necessity. This should be done through an interactive form-processing tool that should culminate into allocation of a unique identification number to the user.

There are many situations where interactive form processing tools can help in this system. The farmer gives goods to the Commission Agent (C.A.) for auction and obtained receipt of delivery of goods. When the auction is done with the consumer and after whole process is completed, expected rate arises then C.A. sold the goods and obtainined money. So in this case money given by the consumer, from that market fee and commission deducted from C.A. and remaining amount goes to consumer. Details of this mentioned on receipt and one copy given to consumer, the other to APMC department and the third are for the farmer. Same copy is maintained by the C.A. also. It can be atomized through form processing tools provided in this system.

Without E-mail services and chat services, no IT enabled agricultural marketing system can be complete. Communication between farmers and C.A. is done and is also important. This helps in proper dissemination of information.

On-line updation of arrivals, sales and prices of various commodities from various markets is very important because without updation recent situation is not known to anybody.

Operation Research tools if properly used can help in optimum solutions i.e., profit maximization solutions regarding sales of goods, transportation cost, resource allocations to the farmer which will help in making cost-effective business.

On supply of information by the farmer through an interactive form, the program based on O.R. tools should give him advise regarding transportation cost of place to place in order to sell goods either in any market or in any state.

Due to climate conditions, rainfall pattern, emergency

attack and increase or decrease in production or productivity, that's why import and export facility should be available.

Market Analysis is the core of any Marketing information system. A user should be able to see future trends of prices and demand, previous pattern, projections and economic indices. Market analysis of future predictions of sales and rates of various commodities from various markets is needed. Graph to show history of market from past 3 - 5 years. Need to generate trend estimators. Time series analysis is also helpful in market analysis.

GIS software is useful in case of mapping analysis. In case of Agricultural Market system, the following maps should be available:

- Map to illustrate locations of MMCs in Marathwada region.
- Map to illustrate locations of SMCs in Marathwada region.

6.6 Requirement specification

In this system, farmer, Commission Agent, APMC organization people and traders like wholesaler, retailer, consumer, dal mill, oil mill and ginning mill plays an important role. Requirement of all the traders is same as far as IT-based Agricultural Marketing system is concerned. APMC have it's own information outlet and they are radio Kendra's, Television stations, District statistical office, Maharashtra state Agril. Marketing Board, Aurangabad and Pune., Director of marketing, Pune., Market Intelligence Branch, Delhi, District Deputy Registrar (Co-operative Society) Parbhani, Assistant Registrar (Co-operative Society) Parbhani. The objective of this system is to establish a system to facilitate a secure, reliable, economical agricultural regulated marketing.

Now the following components are taken in to consideration in order to identify requirements independently:

1. Farmer module
2. Commission Agent module
3. Traders module
4. APMC organization module and

5. APMC information outlets module.

Implementation of Agricultural Marketing subsystem would require

- Development of software at each module.
- Development of Application Programming Interfaces.
- Development of Message formats. (as per the need of application, forms may convert in the form of message formats.)
- Software access by using user-id and password in case of first 1-4 module.
- Software access in case of module 5 by using smart card.

We will discuss the above modules one by one.

6.6.1 Farmer module

Farmer requires a lot of information as we have stated in 6.3. The farmer is unable to purchase computer with Internet connection. To solve this problem, we may suggest Information kiosks or E-seva where Internet facility is available for the farmers at his village. Only to hit particular website, create our own username and password to use frequently, login with user-id and password and use the facilities available on the site. Training should be providing in order to handle web site and site information should be bilingual. So here minimum requirement is that farmer should be literate.

The following facilities would be required in the software:

<u>Farmer should be able to access information on:</u> daily arrivals and prices of various commodities from various markets, form processing tools, chat session, newsletter etc.

<u>Electronic sale mechanism between farmer and C.A.:</u> The farmer would perform the following steps:

1. Login with user-id and password.
2. Click to sale.
3. Choose the C.A. from the list with appropriate market.
4. Fill up the form with entries include name, goods name, quantity, expected rate and address.

5. APMC would take decision over the form and sends confirmation or rejection message to farmer.
6. If form is rejected by APMC then again start with step 3.
7. Goods sent to C.A. by farmer via transport services.
8. C.A. sends goods received slip to farmer.

Inward forms

- Token receipt (for cotton).
- Receipt of goods received (for grain market).

Inward report

- After settlement, detail slip would be given C.A.

6.6.2 Commission Agent module

In this module, the following factors are taken into consideration.

Business rules:

- Market fee = 1%
- Supervision charges = 0.05%
- Commission of C.A. = 2.90 %
- Hamali = 1.85 %
- Tolai = 1.40 %

E-auction:

- Expected rate supplied by Traders.
- Auction software would display current higher rate.
- Software would generate auto reply of rate to the traders.
- Again trader would supply the rate.

This activity would be continued until the auction is finalized on the same day. Final report would be generated and supplied to the traders. Auction time would be parameterized.

Electronic - Money flow transaction from C.A. to farmer:

1. Farmer and C.A. would trust in APMC and should have account holder of specific bank and having debit or credit

card.

2. C.A. sends money details to farmer and APMC.
3. Farmer should send name, account number of bank, credit card number and address to APMC.
4. C.A. credits the amount of farmer in account of APMC.
5. APMC credits the amount in account of farmer.

Electronic - Money flow transaction from C.A. to APMC

1. C.A. and APMC organization should have account holder of specific bank and having debit or credit card.
2. C.A. sends sale and market fee details to APMC.
3. APMC should send account name, debit card number of bank and address to C.A.
4. C.A. Credits the market fee on account of APMC.

Outward forms

- Arrival details receipt (To APMC organization).
- Receipt of goods received (To farmer).

Outward Report

- After auction, bill would be generated and given to trader and APMC organization.
- After settlement, detail slip would be given to farmer and APMC.

Database design

Structure 1: Arrival details receipt

Column name	Type	Length	M/O	Key
Date	Date		M	
Name of C.A.	Varchar2	100	M	P.K
Variety	Varchar2	35	M	
Bags	Number	10	M	
Rate / quintal	Number	10	M	
Purchaser name	Varchar2	100	M	

M/O: Mandatory / Optional

P.K: Primary Key

Structure 2: Receipt of goods received

Column name	Type	Length	M/O	Key
Date	Date		M	
Name of C.A.	Varchar2	100	M	P.K.
Name of farmer	Varchar2	100	M	
Place of farmer	Varchar2	100	M	
Mode of transport	Varchar2	100	O	
Type of goods	Varchar2	35	O	
Average weight	Number	10	M	

Structure 3: After auction, bill would be generated and given to trader and APMC organization.

Column name	Type	Length	M/O	Key
Date	Date		M	
Name of C.A.	Varchar2	100	M	P.K.
Name of purchaser	Varchar2	100	M	
Type of commodity	Varchar2	35	M	P.K.
Number of bags	Number	10	M	
Weight in quintal (1)	Number	10	M	
Rate per quintal (2)	Number	10	M	
Price (3)= (1) * (2)	Number	20	M	
Market fee in % (4)	Number	10	M	
Supervision and gorakshan charges in % (5)	Number	10	M	
Net total paid by trader (6) = (3)+(4)+(5)	Number	20	M	

Structure 4: After settlement, detail slip would be given to farmer and APMC.

Column name	Type	Length	M/O	Key
Date	Date		M	
Name of farmer	Varchar2	100	M	P.K.
Place of farmer	Varchar2	100	M	
Type of commodity	Varchar2	35	M	F.K
Weight in quintal (1)	Number	10	M	
Rate per quintal (2)	Number	10	M	
Price (3) = (1) * (2)	Number	10	M	

Column name	Type	Length	M/O	Key
Commission of C.A. in % (4)	Number	5	M	
Hamali in % (5)	Number	5	M	
Tolai in % (6)	Number	5	M	
Total expenditure (7) = (4)+(5)+(6)	Number	10	M	
Net amount goes to farmer (8) = (3) – (7)	Number	10	M	

F.K.: Foreign key

6.6.3 Traders module

In this module, the following factors are important.

Electronic buy mechanism between Trader and C.A.: Trader would perform the following steps:

1. Login with user-id and password.
2. Click to buy.
3. Choose the C.A. from the list with appropriate market.
4. Trader sends request to buy goods.
5. C.A. sends market rates to Trader.
6. If rates are feasible, then fill up the form with entries include name, goods name, quantity, and address otherwise go to step 3.
7. Goods send by C.A. through confirmation by APMC to Trader using transport services.
8. Trader sends goods received acknowledgement / negative acknowledgement to APMC.

E - Money flow transaction from Trader to C.A

1. Trader and C.A. would trust on APMC and should have account holder of specific bank and having debit or credit card.
2. C.A. should send money details to Trader and APMC.
3. C.A. should send name, account number of bank, credit card number and address to APMC.

4. Trader credits the amount on account of APMC.
5. APMC credits the amount on account of C.A.

Inward Report

- After auction, bill would be given by C.A.

6.6.4 APMC organization module

This is the major module where lot of processing is required that includes:

E- up-gradation facility:

- Data entry operator would look into the arrival detail slip sent by C.A.
- Enter data into the database as per variety of goods.
- Provide online access to user.

Accounting:

Use arrivals detail receipt and prepare summary of daily arrival and prices.

Forms required

- Application form to obtain permission from APMC to work as a Commission Agent.
- Agreement form.
- Form for licensing.
- Form for license renewal.

Outward forms

- Weekly report of Agricultural Commodities Prices, Arrivals and Market Trends at the Regulated Market.(To Marketing Research Officer, Pune and Divisional Joint Registrar (C.S.) Aurangabad.)
- Weekly return of stocks, arrivals, outgoing quantities and prices of Agricultural commodities. (To Marketing Intelligence Branch, Delhi and Marketing Research Officer, Pune)
- Token receipt. (To farmer).
- Market rates. (To Radio station or Television station or

Newspaper agency.)

Inward forms

- Arrival details receipt.

Inward Reports

- After auction, bill would be given by C.A.
- After settlement, detail slip would be given by C.A.

Report generation

- Summary of daily arrival and prices

Application Programming Interface (API):

The major aim is to exchange the messages / files between various nodes like C.A. node, APMC organization node and APMC information outlets. This exchange of message will be in the form of a pre-defined structure.

Two types of API's required to facilitate exchange of information are described below:

1) **'SenderAPI'** helpful to send the messages. First of all receive the message and store it in a particular directory or database and pickup it.
2) **'ReceiverAPI'** is a daemon process , which is continuously active in memory and works like a TSR, so it should be protected from memory.

Security

The secure system must have internal and external controls. The system will provide end-to-end security and requirement of:

- System will ensure that only authenticated users are given access as per their security profiles. The profile will include user details, login id, digital id and access privileges.
- Files created by software are stored in particular directory and is immediately archived so that any user does not alter its content.
- Audit files are backed up daily.
- Incoming and outgoing files and messages would be authenticated.

- To check the integrity of the message to guarantee that the message has not been modified during transmits.
- Access to database by using login and password.
- Administrator should not have access facility of database.
- Data stored in database with secured validation techniques.
- Data stored in database with store and stamp.
- Backup facility should not be menu driven.
- No need to maintain database for a long time, automatically purge it and before that alert a kind of message.
- Mirror imaging facility – to replicate the one more copy of data.
- Firewall's software – to control unauthorized access or malfunctioning.
- Virus protection – virus detection software will be installed on the server to minimize the risk of infection and its damages.
- User – three unsuccessful attempts will lock the customer.
- Uninterruptible power supply.
- Server should be in limited access.

Database design

Structure 5: Weekly report of Agricultural Commodities Prices, Arrivals and Market Trends at the Regulated Market.

Column name	Type	Length	M/O	Key
Commodity	Varchar2	35	M	P.K.
Variety	Varchar2	35	M	
Most common price per quintal	Number	10	M	
Arrivals during the week in quintal	Number	10	M	
Valuation	Number	10	M	P.K.
Arrivals 1st day upto end of this week	Number	10	M	
Valuation of arrivals from 1st day upto end of this week	Number	10	M	

Structure 6: Weekly return of stocks, arrivals, outgoing quantities and prices of Agricultural commodities.

Column name	Type	Length	M/O	Key
Name of commodity (1)	Varchar2	25	M	P.K.
Code (2)	Varchar2	10	M	P.K.
Stock at the beginning of the week (3)	Number	10	M	
From village (4)	Number	10	M	
From other markets (5)	Number	10	M	
Total (6)=(4)+(5)	Number	20	M	P.K.
For local use (7)	Number	10	M	
Dispatches outstation (8)	Number	10	M	
Total (9)=(7)+(8)	Number	20	M	
Stock at the end of the week (10)=(3)+(6)-(9)	Number	10	M	P.K.
Week ending wholesale price per quintal for most common variety (11)	Number	10	O	
Remarks (12)	Varchar2		O	

Structure 7: Token receipt.

Column name	Type	Length	M/O	Key
Date	Date		M	
Token number	Number	5	M	P.K.
Ginning name	Varchar2	100	M	
Farmer's name	Varchar2	100	M	
Place of farmer	Varchar2	50	M	
Mode of travel	Varchar2	100	O	
Type of cotton	Varchar2	100	O	
Vehicle No.	Number	35	M	
Chungi No.	Number	35	M	P.K.

Structure 8: Market rates.

Column name	Type	Length	M/O	Key
Date	Date		M	
Variety of goods	Varchar2	100	M	P.K.
Min. rate	Number	10	M	P.K.
Max. rate	Number	10	M	P.K.
To.	Varchar2	250	M	

Structure 9: Summary of daily arrival and prices

Column name	Type	Length	M/O	Key
Variety of goods	Varchar2	100	M	P.K.
Total no. of bags	Number	10	M	
Min rate	Number	10	M	P.K.
Max rate	Number	10	M	P.K.
Average rate	Number	20	M	
Total cost	Number	20	M	

6.6.5 APMC information outlet module:

Information received at various places in the Inward form.

Inward forms

- Weekly report of Agricultural Commodities Prices, Arrivals and Market Trends at the Regulated Market. (for Marketing Research Officer, Pune, Divisional Joint registrar (C.S.) Aurangabad.)
- Weekly return of stocks, arrivals, outgoing quantities and prices of Agricultural commodities. (for Market Intelligence Branch, Delhi and Marketing Research Officer, Pune)
- Market rates. (for Radio station or Television station or Newspaper agency)

The same System administration tools are required as mentioned in 6.6.4.

The same Security tools are required as mentioned in 6.6.4.

6.7 Regulated Agricultural Market viewed as Neural Nework:

Relation between supply, demand and prices are complex and nonlinear. This is true under any market environment and

Regulated Agricultural Markets cannot be exceptions to this. Regulated Agricultural Markets are a well supervised network of trading units where information on arrivals and prices are closely monitored (Mogul (1989), Chandel (1980), Pokale (1994)). Any information system for such a network should be capable of recognizing the pattern of arrivals and quickly estimate the future prices. The problem can possibly be formulated as

- A dynamical system
- A Neural Network
- Fuzzy-Dynamical system.

A dynamical system would require determination of nonlinear functional relations between arrivals and rates of increase in prices. Considering the fact that market forces are quite complex determining these functions would be a very difficult task. This prompts one to look for a model-free approach as a more ideal choice under circumstances.

The Regulated Marketing system for Agricultural Products constitutes a Network of markets. Trading activities in each of the markets affects prices at all the other markets with varied degrees. Problem of formulation of the arrival-prices information systems for the Regulated Markets has been a problem of interest of Economists over many years. No satisfactory approaches seem to have emerged so far. A discussion of possible alternative formulations of the problem is discussed in this study.

The Regulated Market System:

A network of markets M_1 , M_2 , M_3 , ..., M_m trading in agricultural products G_1 , G_2 , G_3 , ..., G_g , is the object under scrutiny here. Since we are concerned with agricultural products we are looking at a situation where the production process itself is more of stochastic process compared to industrial products where production takes place under comparatively a more deterministic environment. When these are administered or regulated by respective market committees all under one statutory supervisory body, we may call the whole network as regulated market system. Traders who buy and sell these goods are all licensed by these regulatory bodies and are bound to perform trading activities as per the regulations (Chandel, 1980). It is mandatory for the market committees to maintain records of the transactions. The agricultural marketing committees have been maintaining regular records of quantum of sales and prices of agricultural goods traded at these markets. The committees surprisingly do not maintain the arrival figures. Thus for any information system the input information available would be

sales a_{ijk} and

prices (per unit) p_{ijk},

Where, suffixes i, j, k stand for ith day, jth market and kth goods.

The Dynamical System:

The first question that naturally arises is why can we not formulate the problem as a classical dynamical system. One can surely associate a dynamical system

$$\dot{\mathbf{p}} = \mathbf{f}(\mathbf{t}, \mathbf{p}, \mathbf{a})$$

$$\dot{\mathbf{a}} = \mathbf{h}(\mathbf{t}, \mathbf{p}, \mathbf{a})$$

where $\mathbf{p} = (p_1, p_2, \ldots\ldots\ldots, p_m)$ is the price vector and $\mathbf{a} = (a_1, a_2, \ldots\ldots\ldots\ldots, a_m)$ is the sales vector , with the marketing system. Obviously every sale affects the prices and every change in price affects the sale. At any given time the vectors **(p, a)** together define the state of the market. Whenever there is a large positive time derivative of the sales vector, one may expect that the market would have entered panic sales state. Whenever there is a large negative gradient of the price vector one may expect that the market has entered a large arrival state. Whenever there is a zero gradient of sales, but the arrivals cannot be assumed to be low, the state is that of hoarding tendency by the traders.

Arriving at appropriate functional forms for **f** and **h** and then examining the stability of the dynamical system would surely be a very difficult task given the various market forces affecting the system and given the state of information that is maintained at the market committees. Traditionally economists have been using the concepts like seasonal indices and time series analysis for analyzing such situations. But such analysis have not been very successful in adequately describing the inter-market relations (Mogul, 1989) . Linearising the relations could be one of the solutions.

More appropriate would be to go for model-free solutions, either in the form of a artificial neural network or a fuzzy dynamical system or may be a combination of both could be a solution. A model-free approach definitely has an advantage over these methods. We examine the marketing system with this object in mind next.

The Artificial Neural Network

This is one possible alternative to the formulation. We may consider the markets , which are members of a group of markets as a field of neurons. In the absence of any predefined ordering, they are related only by synaptic connections between them. Lack of topological structure in the fields of neurons is also described as **zeroth-order topology** (Kohonen (1988)) . Markets are continuously communicating with each other shown in fig 6.3. Arrival of goods at a market M_1 activates the market.

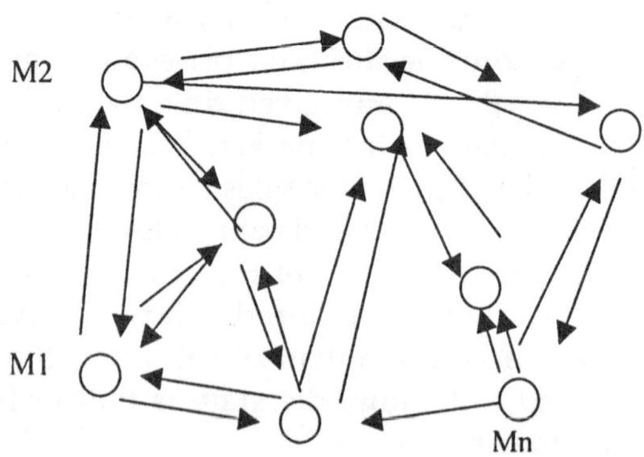

Figure 6.3: Markets are continuously communicating with each other:

If at any moment arrival at a market is below a threshold, then the activation is so feeble that the perturbations exponentially die fast and no changes take place in prices. In other words no signals are exchanged between the markets when the arrivals are below a threshold. If the arrival is above a thresh hold signals reach every other market resulting in changes in the prices. The readjustment of prices in its own affects the tendency to trade at the respective markets affecting the future arrivals. If the arrivals are equal to the threshold we may expect the earlier signal to continue to be effective without any change.

Each individual market can also be viewed as an artificial neural network, where the traders are the neurons. Arrival of goods at any individual trading point activates the market. The activation leads to trading activities. Signals exchange between numerous trading points within the market. This affects prices at all the trading points. The exchanges ultimately settle into a series of negotiated sales and prices.

These observation can be sumarized into:

Associated threshold signal functions

$$Si(\Delta p_i^{\,k}) = \begin{cases} 1 & \text{if } \Delta p_j^{\,k} > U_i \\ Si(\Delta p_i^{\,k-1}) & \text{if } \Delta p_i^{\,k} = U_i \\ -1 & \text{if } \Delta p_i^{\,k} < U_i \end{cases}$$

and

$$Sj(\Delta a_j^{\,k}) = \begin{cases} 1 & \text{if } \Delta a_j^{\,k} > V_j \\ Sj(\Delta a_j^{\,k-1}) & \text{if } \Delta a_j^{\,k} = V_j \\ -1 & \text{if } \Delta a_j^{\,k} < V_j \end{cases}$$

where $\mathbf{p}_j^{\,k}$ are the pricés at time step k and $\mathbf{a}_j^{\,k}$ are the sales . Suffixes i and j correspond to the markets. Threshold values for price differential and sales differential are given by numbers $\mathbf{U}_i$ and $\mathbf{V}_j$.

The exact information on arrivals is seldom available at markets. Information that is actually available with the market committee constitutes the pair (a, p) where a is the quantum sold and p is the rate at which sold, i.e. the sale price. Hence the market committee has to depend only on these values as the state variables indicating the stateof the market at any time. Sales are the culmination of the activation. As a result of the activation the market may enter into different states. Since we have only finite number of markets we will have only finite number of states . A state would now correspond to a point in the bipolar n-cube

$\{-1,1\}^n$,

This bi-directionalexchange of signals continues for a short period and the market settles down quickly to a new state. With a fresh arrival at any of the markets again this process is repeated. The bivalent signal functions can emulate highly complex asynchronous state change patterns. The mechanism would be as under:

At any moment different markets can decide to compare their current activation to their threshold. They need not do all at once. At each moment any subset of the markets (neurons) may change state. The choice of subsets will be probabilistic. Each neuron behaves as a scalar stochastic process. The network as such behaves as a vector stochastic process.

Without loss of generality we assume that the state changes are synchronous, i.e. we can update the state changes at a time. This is justifiable as state changes in agricultural markets are generally assessed only after the business hours each day. The States into which the market can exist could be classified as PANIC SALE, HIGH SALE, LOW SALE, TENDENCY TO HOARD etc.

Data Collection:

Six Main Market Committees (MMC) around Parbhani have been surveyed so far (Names and distances between the markets are indicated in table 2). Data collected is based on the parameter like sales and unit prices of different crops and maintained by APMC . Data over the last three years from these markets is used for the study. Two years data have been used to train the system. Table 6.1 consists of names of the markets, crops and year of data.

Table 6.1: Name of the markets, crops and year of data.

Name of the markets	Used crops	Year of data
Parbhani	Jawar,Wheat,Tur,Mug	Oct 96 - Sept 99
Purna	Jawar,Wheat,Tur,Mug	Oct 96 - Sept 99
Basmat	Jawar,Wheat,Tur,Mug	Oct 96 - Sept 99
Jintur	Jawar,Wheat,Tur,Mug	Oct 96 - Sept 99
Gangakhed	Jawar,Wheat,Tur,Mug	Oct 96 - Sept 99
manwat	Jawar,Wheat,Tur,Mug	Oct 96 - Sept 99

Stability Aspects:

One may establish easily that the system can be expected to be only in those states which are either asymptotically stable or stable. Possibility of instability is ruled out.

Learning Process:

The market system is expected to remember the asymptotically stable paths experienced earlier for recognition of patterns in future. The patterns remembered possibly as **Bi-directional Associative Memory (BAM)** [Mathai, 1989, Wang 1990]. matrices.

Recall Process:

In the recall process , the BAM matrices help the system in recognizing the ultimate asymptotically stable states and predicting them well in advance given a partial path. Such a process is very important from the point of planning controlled supply systems of essential food items.

Analysis:

Appendix 2 consists of sixty-four states and stability of the crop. In that, as per State 8 Jawar markets are asymptotically stable after two weeks, Wheat markets are stable, Tur markets are asymptotically stable after three weeks and Mug markets are asymptotically stable after two weeks. 1 indicates Stable state of the market and 2, 3 and 4 indicates Asymptotic stable state of the markets.

Results:

Synapse generated by Unsupervised learning method are given in figure 6.4. The matrices Mi reported in the table corresponds to the following situation:

$$X^T M = Y$$

Where X^T is the vector given by signals corresponding to arrivals and Y corresponds to the rate signals. This is considered as the forward pass as price signals are generated from the arrival signal. The Backward pass is given by

$$Y^T M^T = X$$

It is observed that, the matrices are all non - symmetric. Hence at any state would be either Stable or Asymptotic stable. Therefore which reflects the inherent nature of the markets. Since there are six markets. Essentially there are $2^6=64$ different states in which the system of market can exist.

M1 synapse generated for jawar crop.

$$M1 = \begin{bmatrix} -2 & -18 & -18 & -4 & -10 & -2 \\ -2 & -6 & -6 & 4 & -2 & 6 \\ -22 & -38 & -38 & -4 & -10 & -14 \\ 6 & 6 & 6 & 4 & 6 & -6 \\ 10 & 2 & 2 & 12 & -6 & -2 \\ -2 & -18 & -18 & -8 & 2 & 18 \end{bmatrix}$$

M2 synapse generated for wheat crop .

$$M2 = \begin{bmatrix} 0 & 10 & 10 & 8 & 0 & -10 \\ 4 & 2 & 2 & 4 & 24 & 2 \\ 0 & 14 & 14 & -8 & 16 & -6 \\ 4 & 14 & 14 & 4 & -4 & 6 \\ -4 & 6 & 6 & -4 & 20 & 6 \\ -10 & -16 & -16 & 22 & -22 & 12 \end{bmatrix}$$

M3 synapse generated for Tur crop .

$$M3 = \begin{bmatrix} 6 & -10 & -10 & 4 & -6 & 0 \\ 2 & 22 & 22 & 0 & 14 & 4 \\ -12 & -16 & -16 & -6 & 0 & -22 \\ 8 & -4 & -4 & 6 & 0 & 2 \\ -12 & 16 & 16 & 10 & 4 & 14 \\ -8 & -4 & -4 & -10 & 8 & 18 \end{bmatrix}$$

M4 synapse generated for Mug crop .

$$M4 = \begin{bmatrix} -26 & -30 & -30 & -30 & -26 & -16 \\ -32 & -28 & -28 & -24 & -12 & -18 \\ -32 & -36 & -36 & -36 & -24 & -34 \\ -26 & -14 & -14 & -14 & -34 & -8 \\ 26 & 10 & 10 & 2 & 26 & 12 \\ -2 & -6 & -6 & 6 & 6 & 8 \end{bmatrix}$$

Figure 6.4: Synapse generated by Unsupervised learning method.

Distinct states were examined for their stability properties. The results are reported in Appendix 2 for the crops under consideration. It is clear that Wheat and jawar are more stable. In case of wheat , no state remain dynamic for more than two weeks whereas in case of Tur , few states were found to remain dynamic about four weeks and in case of mung , some of the states remain dynamic in three weeks, showing that more instability compared to jawar and wheat.

Table 6.2: A typical Asymptotic stable case of State 45 in case of Tur.

Markets	S(Δa)	S(Δp)	S(Δa)	S(Δp)	S(Δa)	S(Δp)	S(Δa)	S(Δp)
Market1	-1	-1	1	-1	1	1	1	1
Market2	1	-1	-1	-1	-1	-1	-1	-1
Market3	1	-1	1	-1	1	-1	1	-1
Market4	-1	-1	-1	-1	-1	1	1	1
Market5	-1	1	-1	-1	-1	-1	-1	-1
Market6	1	-1	1	-1	-1	-1	-1	-1

It is clear from the table 6.2; state 45 remain dynamic about four weeks.

Table 6.3: Co-efficient of variation in the considered crops

Name of the markets / Crops	Jawar		Wheat		Tur		Mug	
	sales	rates	sales	rates	sales	rates	sales	rates
Parbhani	163.09	12.79	207.57	19.13	156.74	15.83	239.24	15.05
Purna	150.26	11.40	140.35	13.92	209.30	21.54	243.17	15.44
Basmat	226.54	8.83	347.01	13.01	316.60	15.52	242.73	13.70
Jintur	85.84	12.58	347.01	15.99	169.83	16.96	297.31	13.33
Gangakhed	135.22	15.03	123.11	13.64	152.38	20.54	263.89	18.82
Manwat	196.36	13.19	212.26	21.46	241.99	17.39	330.95	17.47
Average	159.55	12.30	229.55	16.19	207.71	17.96	269.54	15.63

It is evident from the Table 6.3 that values of coefficient of variation of tur and mug show a larger variation compared to jawar and wheat.

Chapter 7

Irrigation Subsystem

7.0 Introduction

The government has invested huge sums of money in irrigation projects of varied sizes, ground water recharging projects. Watershed development is a top priority programme of central and state governments. Farmers themselves have been investing in farm level irrigation projects. There are quite a few industries that produce irrigation equipment and market them. Many research workers are constantly engaged in studying irrigation requirements of various crops and better methods of optimally allocating water to various activities. Most of all these are always many irrigation scheduling and planning problems that farmers keep posing. Dividing water between civil utilities, farm activities and industrial uses is always a problem.

As far as farming is concerned, replenishing the soil-water deficit by applying irrigation water is referred to as irrigation. Adequate and timely supply of irrigation water is one of the basic inputs for obtaining potential crop yield. Very often it is the most important limiting factor in crop production. Considering all these aspects, it may be said that like marketing, an independent information subsystem for people involved in irrigation activities is a must. It should revolve round providing information on

- Irrigation for agriculture
- Irrigation for electricity generation
- Supply of water to industry
- Drinking water supply

Information availability in local language is again a must considering the fact that rural people and farmers are the major target group. In this chapter we will consider the design aspects of such information systems.

7.1 Irrigation related websites

Information on Irrigation currently available on the following sites:

http://www.cimis.water.ca.gov (California Irrigation Management Information System - Department water resources),

http://forages.orst.edu/IS/AIS/enfpmain.cfm?PageID=250 (Regional Irrigation information),

http://www.cm.ksc.co.th/~bruns/9_info.html (Distributed Information System for farmer managed irrigation),

http://www.fao.org/ag/agl/aglw/aquastat/regions/lac/index5.stm (Land and Water development division),

http://www.vl-irrigation.org/cms/index.php?id=137 (Virtual library irrigation).

In most cases, the information available on irrigation equipment, list of dealers, utilization etc but information specific to particular region, informationon irrigation scheduling, water rotation, and usage of water is not available on the sites that are required with high importance.

7.2 Suggested Design specifications

One should be able to design an Irrigation Information system, complete within itself but of varying extents as per the need identified, either as an independent information system or as a subsystem of a larger Agricultural Information System. An attempt to classify situations and associate appropriate Design specifications from the ones defined in Chapter 4 is made in the following table.

Table 7.1: Design specifications on Irrigation

Design specification (As Defined in Chapter 4)	Agencies (Which may run and maintain)	Target Groups of Users
Design specifications 1 and 2	Small Irrigation Project Managers, Small Watershed Units, Irrigation equipment dealers, Irrigation Consulting Engineers	Limited Clientele generally restricted by Geographic area

Design specification (As Defined in Chapter 4)	Agencies (Which may run and maintain)	Target Groups of Users
Design specification 3	Larger Farm Cooperatives, Command Area Development Authority, Irrigation Companies	Same as above
Design specification 4	State Department of Irrigation	Practically every one connected with irrigation, farmers, traders, research workers, planners, and policymakers.

The design aspects of Irrigation Systems, based on Design specification 4, are discussed in this chapter, the other Design specifications generally being subsets of this larger Design specification, require no specific elaboration. As in the last chapter once again we concentrate only on the software aspects, because hardware aspects have been already discussed adequately in Chapter 4.

7.3 Data Warehousing Strategies

The most difficult aspect in any information system design is to identify agencies that produce basic data, establish a seamless connection between these production units and encourage them to share data, establish common processing channels, and decide common protocols so that there is no duplication in storage and processing efforts.

It is very much evident that data are generated continuously in various command area development authorities, major and minor irrigation projects, ground water survey agencies, soil survey and classification agencies and remote sensing and GIS data producing agencies. The data are huge. On the basis of our study we could classify the data, places of their origin, storage facilities as under:

Table 7.2: Data warehouse requirement

Data Item	Type and nature	Storage	Upgradation requirement	Place of Origin
Water availability distribution policies	Numeric Varying with time	Huge capacity required, pose warehousing problems	Weekly preferred	CADA, Irrigation Project Offices
Market regulations, tax rules,(text/ documents)	Text/ Documents Almost static	Not much of a problem	Annually or only when they change	
Locations of canals, distributaries, dams, lift irrigation facilities	Digitized Maps Geographic Information not very dynamic	Not much of a problem	Annually or only when they change	CADA offices, Geographical Survey
Registrations, Licensing	Varying with time	Moderate volumes, should not pose problems	Online recording and Up gradation	State Irrigation Department

7.4 Information content

We have already identified general components of information contents of different Design specifications in Chapter 4. We will not discuss how systems based on Design specification 1 and 2 should be designed in respect of contents. These Design specifications being small and recommendable for systems run by individuals and small organizations their information contents should be more driven by the specific interests of the agencies running the system. Design specification 4 which is recommended for semi - government organizations like large command area development authortites, and state department of irrigation, require more specific identification and more scientific approach with regards to contents design. Hence they are discussed here. As we have already discussed in the last section some of the contents could be raw data, some could be information generated using this data, some static in nature and some dynamic in nature with varying degree of dynamicity. Repeated discussion sessions were held with informants to arrive at a comprehensive list of essential contents of the irrigation aspects of the information system:

- Static Information Contents:
  1. List of regional major, medium and minor projects.
  2. List of Command Area Development Authorities.
  3. Water charges as per government norms.
  4. Laws regarding digging wells, tube wells, and grown water lifting.
  5. Laws, taxation rules concerning distribution and sharing of water
  6. Irrigation Equipment Manufacturers and their addresses
  7. Water Quality regulations and Norms.
  8. Contacts of Quality control agencies and Laboratories
- Dynamic or Frequently Upgradeable Contents:
  1. Water availability status in various reservoirs
  2. GIS on ground water availability
  3. GIS on drainage properties of soils
  4. GIS on water-holding capacities of soils
  5. GIS on AMC classes
  6. GIS showing slopes, waterways, tanks
  7. Adequate number of FAQs
  8. Adequate number of HOWTOs,
  9. Newsletter (weekly or bi-weekly)
  10. Links to important websites,
  11. Annual reports of Command area developments
- CGI assisted dynamic facilities:
  1. Water tax collection.
  2. Water requirement applications, allocation decisions.
  3. Monitoring water storage at reservoirs.
  4. Water charge computation tools.
  5. Water requirement computation tools for various crops.

6. Watershed developments programmes, locations, cropping maps.
7. Mail services.
8. Chat Services.
9. Predictors, trend estimators for availability of water in different seasons.

The list provided above is only a framework. This frame can serve as a template to any one who wants to design contents for his info system. According to the scope in mind and need of targeted users the designer can pick and choose.

7.5 Utilities of the contents item by item

Updated information on major, medium and minor projects, information on Command area development Authorities are required so that farmers can know from where and to what extent they are going to receive irrigation support.

Online applications for irrigation water allotments will reduce the time gaps between requisitioning and actual allocation reducing risk arising because of time losses.

Properly updated water charges as per government norms are most important for farmers who are the consumers of water. Laws regarding digging wells, tube wells, and ground water lifting laws, taxation rules concerning distribution and sharing of water help a farmer in planning his irrigation strategies.

Irrigation Equipment Manufacturers and their addresses, Water Quality regulations and Norms, Contacts of Quality control agencies and Laboratories are all part of management information needed by a farmer. These are also important for irrigation equipment dealers and designers.

Newsletters in the electronic form will keep the users informed about changing policies, important events etc. Frequently asked questions (FAQ) and HOWTOs are electronic documents generally indexed and provisions of links to help quick electronic search. FAQs and HowTos should be on modalities of trade, membership, regarding license and renewal, and so on.

Providing links to other similar sites is also very important because no Agricultural irrigation system can be complete in itself. This will guide the user in acquiring the more information whenever needed. Reliable E-mail services and chat services are essential a component of any IT enables system.

Operation Research tools, time series analysis techniques are required in the background for analysis and producing usable advises to water allocation planners.

7.6 Expert System on Irrigation

We may use Expert System on Irrigation in order to solve the problems like allocation of water, water rotations etc. Figure 7.1 illustrates the players in the Irrigation Expert system.

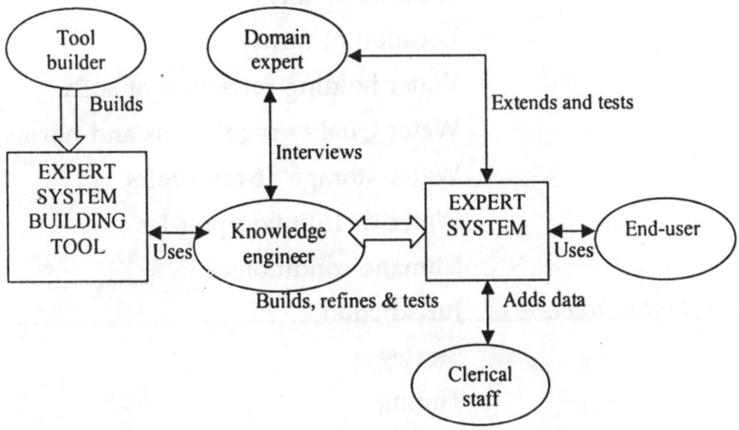

Figure 7.1: Players in the Irrigation Expert system.

The roles of above players would be:

Tool builder - The person who designs and builds the expert-system-building tool.

Expert system building tool - The programming language and support package used to build the expert system.

Domain expert - The person who is trained and proficient in problem-solving in a particular domain.

Knowledge engineer - The person who designs and builds the expert system.

Expert system – A computer program using expert knowledge to attain high levels of performance in a narrow problem area.

The following concepts are needed to produce a solution:

Project goal –	Evaluate irrigation scheduling cases
Main problem –	Determine water requirement of farm based on soil type, climatic conditions, Weather report and type of commodity
Sub problems –	Calculating special water wastages
	Calculating general water wastages
	Determine actual requirement of water
Problem characteristics –	Incomplete data
Data –	Weather report
	Location of farm
	Water holding capacities of soils
	Water Quality regulations and norms
	Water storage at reservoirs
	Water distribution policies
	Climatic conditions
Important concepts –	Jurisdiction
	Strategy
	Timing
	Type of irrigation
Solution –	Optimum allocation of water at appropriate time with cost

Chapter 8

Research and Education Subsystem

8.0 Introduction

Research and education are at the core of development of any sector. Research is the activity where the 'information' is generated for the whole of the agricultural information system. Research and education are complementary to each other. In Chapter 5 we had naturally assumed interaction between a research worker and a farmer, possibly through the extension agencies or in the modern system supported by a direct communication link. The people involved in agricultural research and education need a good information system for supporting their activities. The very fact that there exists an independent academy for Agricultural Research Management at Hyderabad is a pointer to the extent and importance of the need.

India spends considerable money on agricultural research and education. The setup is quite large with more than 25,000 scientists and teachers working in 45 central institutes, 4 National Institutes with Deemed University status, 4 National Bureaus, 30 National Research Centers, 10 Project Directorates, 80 All India coordinated research Projects, 34 State Agricultural Universities, 1 Central Agricultural University, 8 Training Centers, 315 Krishi Vigyan Kendras (as on Jan 2001). These institutes have established more than 290 zonal research stations and regional research stations to take care of research needs of specific regions, specific geographic and environmental conditions (Alam, 2001). The SAUs have been imparting education to students all over the country in Agriculture, Animal Sciences, Fisheries, Forestry, Agricultural Engineering, Food Science and Nutrition, Home Science and many more related fields.

Agricultural Information System therefore must have a

research and teaching subsystem to deal with needs of students, parents, teachers and researchers.

8.1 Website of ICAR organizations SAU's

The SAUs are major partners in growth & development of Agricultural Research and Education under National Agricultural Research System. Table 8.1 gives a list of portals and websites of ICAR institutions and the SAU's.

S. No	Name and Email Address	Address
1	Acharya N G Ranga Agricultural University (APAU) Email: root@apau.ap.nic.in	Rajendranagar Hyderabad Andhra Pradesh PIN 500030
2	Agricultural University Udaipur (AUU) Email:	University Campus Udaipur Rajasthan PIN 313001
3	Assam Agriculture University (AAU) Email: vc@aau.ren.nic.in Web Site: http://www.aau.ac.in/	Jorhat Assam PIN 785013
4	Bidhan Chandra Krishi Vishva Vidyalaya (BCKVV) Email: root@bckv.wb.nic.in	Haringhatta PO Mohanpur Nadia West Bengal PIN 741246
5	Birsa Agricultural University (BAU) Email: root@bau.bih.nic.in Web Site: www.icar.org.in/birsa/BAU.htm	Kanke Ranchi Bihar PIN 834006
6	CCS Haryana Agricultural University (HAU) Email: root@hau.pnp.nic.in Web Site: hau.nic.in	Hisar Haryana PIN 125004
7	Central Agricultural University (CAU) Email:	JROISEMBA Imphal Manipur PIN 795001
8	Chandra Shekhar Azad University of Agriculture & Technology (CSAUT) Email: csauknp@hotmail.com Web Site: http://www.csauk.org/	Kanpur Uttar Pradesh PIN 208002
9	Dr. Panjabrao Deshmukh Krishi Vishwa Vidyalaya (PKV) Email: vc@pdkv.mah.nic.in Web Site: pdkv.mah.nic.in	Krish Nagar Akola Maharashtra PIN 444104

S. No	Name and Email Address	Address
10	Govind Ballabh Pant University of Agriculture and Technology (GBPAU&T) Email: root@gbpuat.ernet.in Web Site: http://www.gbpuat.ac.in/	Pantnagar Uttar Pradesh PIN 263145
11	Gujarat Agricultural University (GAU) Email: gau@gau.guj.nic.in Web Site: gau.guj.nic.in	Dantiwada Sardar Krishi Nagar Gujarat PIN 385506
12	Himachal Pradesh Krishi Vishwa Vidyalaya (HPKVV) Email: root@hpkv.hp.nic.in Web Site: hpkv.hp.nic.in	Palampur Himachal Pradesh PIN 176062
13	Indira Gandhi Krishi Vishwa Vidyalaya (IGKVV) Email: adr@zrcmp01.mp.nic.in	Krishak Nagar Raipur Madhya Pradesh PIN 492012
14	Jawaharlal Nehru Krishi Vishwa Vidyalaya (JNKVV) Email: root@jnau.mp.nic.in	Jabalpur Madhya Pradesh PIN 482004
15	Kerala Agricultural University (KAU) Email: kauhqr@ren.nic.in	Vellanikkara Trichur Kerala PIN 680654
16	Konkan Krishi Vidyapeeth (KKV) Email: root@kkv.ren.nic.in	Dopali Maharashtra PIN 415712
17	Mahatama Phule Krishi Vidyapeeth (MPKV) Email: kvmp@ren.nic.in Web Site: mpkv.mah.nic.in	Rahuri Maharashtra
18	Marathwada Agricultural University (MAU) Email: mau@ren.nic.in	Parbhani Maharashtra PIN 431402
19	Narendra Dev University of Agriculture and Technology (NDUAT) Email: nduat@up.nic.in	Faizabad Uttar Pradesh PIN 224229
20	Orissa University of Agiculture & Technology (OUAT) Email: root@uat.ori.nic.in Web Site: bhub.ori.nic.in/ouat	Bhubaneswar Orissa PIN 751001
21	Punjab Agricultural University (PAU) Email: root@pau.chd.nic.in	Ludhiana Punjab PIN 141004

S. No	Name and Email Address	Address
22	Rajasthan Agricultural University (RAU) Email: root@raub.raj.nic.in	Bikaner Rajasthan PIN 334002
23	Rajendra Agricultural University (RAU) Email: rau@bih.nic.in	Pusa Samastipur Bihar PIN 848125
24	Sher-e-Kashmir University of Agricultural Sciences & Technology (SKUAS&T, Jammu) Email:	Camp Office, Railway Road Jammu Jammu & Kashmir PIN 180004
25	Sher-e-Kashmir University of Agricultural Sciences & Technology (SKUAS&T, Kashmir) Email: anwar_alam@jk.nic.in Web Site: www.icar.org.in/sherk/welcome.htm	Post Box 262, GPO Srinagar Shalimar Campus, Srinagar Kashmir PIN 191121
26	Tamil Nadu Agricultural University (TNAU) Email: root@tnau.tn.nic.in	Coimbatore Tamil Nadu PIN 641003
27	Tamil Nadu Veterinary & Animal Sciences University (TNV&ASU) Email: root@tnvasu.tn.nic.in	Chennai Tamil Nadu PIN 600007
28	University of Agricultural Sciences (UAS) Email: Web Site: uasbng.kar.nic.in	Bangalore Karnataka PIN 560065
29	University of Agricultural Sciences (UAS) Email: root@uasd.kar.nic.in aris@uasd.net Web Site: http://www.uasd.net/	Krishi Nagar Dharwad Karnataka PIN 580005
30	West Bengal University of Animal & Fishery Sciences (WBUA&FS) Email:	68, Khudi Ram Bose Sarani, Belgachia Kolkata West Bengal PIN 700037
31	Yashwant Singh Parmar University of Horticulture & Forestry (YSPUH&F) Email: vc@yspuhf.ren.nic.in Web Site: http://www.ysparmaruniversity.org/	Solan Himachal Pradesh PIN 173230

Source: www.icar.org.in

It is very obvious that most of the contents are of static nature. Secondly they tend to give information on administrative, contact, guidelines, literature etc but very few online facilities are available for use of students, parents and teachers.

8.2 Suggested models

Small institutions like KVK's and Colleges may opt for models 1 or 2 depending on the number of targeted population and the regional requirements. SAUs may think of going for a research and education system based on Model 4 or 5 to strengthen the current system. The design aspects of research and education systems based on model 4 or 5 are discussed in this chapter. Many institutions are running websites of their own as can be seen from the list provided in the last section. However the content designing leaves many areas to be covered.

8.3 Information content

We have already identified components of information contents of different models in Chapter 4. We will not discuss again how research and education systems based on model 1 and 2 should be designed in respect of contents. Models 4 and 5 that are recommended for large organizations may require more specific identification with regards to contents design. Hence they are discussed here.

- They should contain the following static pages:
    1. Newsletter (weekly or bi-weekly),
    2. Scientific journal (quarterly or half yearly),
    3. Research bulletin,
    4. Announcement of training, workshop or conference or seminar etc.
    5. Recent News,
    6. List of private and government agricultural colleges,
    7. List of agricultural schools,
    8. List of research centers and research stations,
    9. Prospectus of institutes

10. Syllabi
11. Rules and Regulations,
12. Adequate number of FAQs,
13. Adequate number of HowTos,
14. List of educational councellors and links to them,
15. GIS showing campus details, How to reach, Transport to and within, Hostel facilities
16. Links to other important sites, and following dynamic facilities:

1. Sharable Scientific Databases
2. Sharable Scientific Documents
3. Students registration, payment of fees
4. Application Form processing tools,
5. Mail service/Char services for members,
6. Distance education/ Virtual classrooms and labs
7. On-line examination facility,
8. Virtual Library (National, Regional)
9. Organization of e-Workshops/ e-Seminars on the net
10. Facility for online national selection tests for admission to cources
11. Online Simulation Experiments designed by top teachers
12. Online Tutorials
13. Examination Results,
14. Video conferencing facilities,
15. Parent / Teachers/ Parent-Teacher / Teacher-student forums.

Now we will discuss a few of the important components:

8.4 Design of static information

Newsletters, Scientific journals, Research bulletins, prospectus, syllabus, academic regulations, addresses of affiliated institutions, FAQs, HowTo,. S pages about announcements of training, workshop or conference or seminar, news and list of agricultural schools and colleges and research stations would be the usual statistic contents.

One of the major objectives of research and education system is direct contact between the researcher and the users. A quick access to a researcher and communication to the expert will solve large number of the problems of the user effectively. Hence any system should provide the list of experts and links to their E-mail addresses. A key to the specialization of the expert is a must.

Providing links to other similar sites is also very important because no system can be complete in itself. This will guide the user in acquiring the more information whenever needed.

8.5 Design of components of dynamic pages

Online registration, examination facilities for the current education system. This should be done through an interactive form-processing tool, which should culminate, into allocation of a unique identification number to the user. There are many situations where interactive form processing tools can help in this system.

Without E-mail services and chat services, no IT enabled research and education system can be complete. Communication between parents, teachers and students is also equally important as communication between researchers and farmers.

Training for inter-prune (student) should be possible using IT enabled services.

On-line examination facility is helpful to retrieve questions from server and students are capable to solve question in his college and answers will be stored on server and after completion of exam, immediately result will be declared on the screen.

Video conferencing tool is useful in establishing virtual classrooms. Classrooms at locations far off from the headquarters.

8.6 Subject grouping and relevant keywords

In this system, the following code and keywords are

required (T. Balaguru (1996)).

1) Agricultural in General.

Code	Agriculture - General aspects
A01	Agriculture development, Agriculture policies, commercial farming, green revolution, white revolution, natural disasters.
	Agricultural Research
A50	Agricultural research, co-ordinated research, planning, research institutions, research management, research policies, research projects.

2) Education, Extension and Information.

Code	Education
C10	Agricultural Education, Curriculum, Educational policies, Educational technology, higher education, manpower, teaching material, teaching methods, vocational training.
	Extension
C20	Appropriate technology, Audio visual aids, demonstration, diffusion of information, exhibitions, extension, extension-activities, extension system, workers, feedback, innovation adoption, mass media, research extension linkages, technology transfer.
	Documentation and Information
C30	Automation, computer applications, computer software, databases, documentation, information needs, information processing, information science, information services, information systems, programming.

8.7 Virtual Library

A library, which has no physical existence, being constructed solely in electronic form or on paper. The building blocks required for such a library may not exist, and the building steps for such a library may not have been tested. These libraries are used in the design and evaluation of possible libraries.

Web enabled services:

Agriculture E - Care web enabled service required in India. E - Care brings together comprehensive out-of-the-box functionality and unsurpassed scalability and performance that would seamlessly integrate with your Customer Relationship Management (CRM) applications or existing business processes. Using E - Care, Support Agents at the call center or help desk be able to assist anyone, anywhere, and resolve technical problems on the spot. The end-result is superior service levels, improved first-call resolution and major cost savings. Web enabled services required for:

- Registration
- Admission
- Results
- Certificates

8.8 Virtual University

The concept that makes it possible to interpret Virtual Education in a holistic way. In recent years the term "Distance Education" has frequently been exchanged with "Virtual Education". Referring to an institution the common phrase used is "Virtual University".

Normally, university constitutes the Administration department, faculty and student. Virtual university would be able to provide E-learning or distance education programme, E - course material, E - results and E - certificates etc.

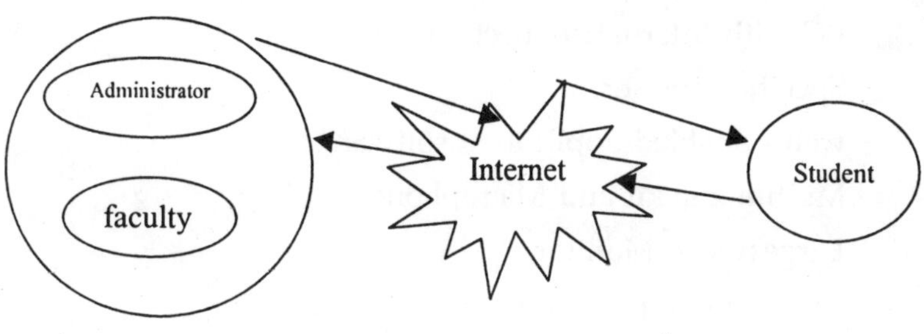

University

Requirement at student side:

PC with Internet connection.

Requirement at University side:

DNS load balancing server or crystal server

Software required for Form processing tools, accounting, certification etc.

Interactive Application software based on CGI programming or Java applets.

Databases, Database Interfaces, Database drivers.

Videoconferencing tool with VCON software.

Multimedia kit and Microphone.

Camera.

API's.

8.9 Virtual Classrooms

Requirement at Virtual Classroom for single user - at your node or at the cyber café:

PC with Internet connection.

Adequate browser with specific version.

web - enabled application software.

Multimedia kit and Microphone.

Videoconferencing tool kit.

Requirement at Organization of a classroom for 20-30 Students:

PC with Internet connection.

Specific browser.

web - enabled application software.

Multimedia kit and Microphone.

Largest size Monitor.

Videoconferencing tool kit.

Requirement at organization of a classroom for about 100 Students:

PC with Internet connection.

Specific browser.

web - enabled application software.

Multimedia kit and Microphone.

LCD display.

Videoconferencing tool kit.

8.10 Web enabled Simulated Experiment (Virtual Lab)

Simulation experiment of leaf analysis:

In this experiment, first of all identify the disease of a leaf by using sensors. Sensor would be capable to extract the characteristics of leaf like pale yellow color, spots, etc. As per the identified disease, software would generate a solution.

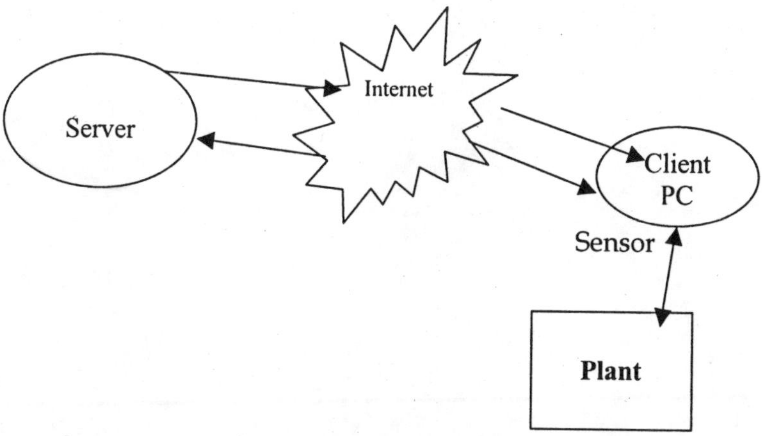

Experiment 1: To identify the disease of a leaf.

Experiment 2: To identify the soil type and its nutritions.

Experiment 3: To identify the water deficiency.

Experiment 4: To note down the observations.

Experiment 5: Suggested solutions in terms of insecticide and pesticide.

Server side:

Corporate website.

Leaf databases.

Software for leaf analysis and for solution provider.

Reports.

Sensor operable software.

Client side:

PC with sensor.

Sensor Interface.

Adequate browser.

Chapter 9
Conclusions

In conclusion, we may state that, there is a need for Agro Information System as established in Chapter two.

The beneficiaries of the system would be Farmers, Research workers, Extension personnel; Agro-based industries, Regulated Agricultural Markets, Government agricultural departments, Research and Education organizational institution, if proper information system are established.

The logistics shown in Chapter three, establishes clearly that, extent of the problem is huge and the beneficiaries are considerably large.

It is very difficult to design a comprehensive Agricultural Information System to meet the requirements of all. Hence a modular approach constituting a sub information system is put forth in Chapter four. Different size models to suit different requirements are proposed here and hardware, software requirements in general have been specified.

A dynamic Farm - Advisory Subsystem has been proposed in Chapter five.

In Chapter six, Importance of Market analysis using Neural Network and time Series analysis has been stressed.

Importance of Expert System has been advocated in Chapter Seven.

Role of Virtual University, Virtual library, Virtual classroom have been emphasized in Chapter eight.

Thus, Agro Information System that is an ever-evolutionary system requires to be modernized with applications of IT technology for benefit of all.

Appendix 1
Sample code of Farm - Advisory system

Section A: Program for user creation in order to login.

```
# include<stdio.h>
# include "cgic.h"
# include <mysql.h>
# include <string.h>
# include <stdlib.h>
MYSQL *conn;
MYSQL_RES *res_set;
MYSQL_ROW row;

int cgiMain() {
char *first,*middle,*last,*village,*taluka,*username;
char *temp,*query,*s1;
int num,i,flag=0;
first = (char *) malloc(25);
middle = (char *) malloc(25);
last = (char *) malloc(25);
village = (char *) malloc(25);
taluka = (char *) malloc(25);
username = (char *) malloc(7);
temp = (char *) malloc(7);
query = (char *) malloc(200);
s1 = (char *) malloc(400);
cgiFormString("first",first,25);
cgiFormString("middle",middle,25);
cgiFormString("last",last,25);
cgiFormString("village",village,25);
cgiFormString("taluka",taluka,25);
cgiFormString("username",username,7);

conn = mysql_init(NULL);
mysql_real_connect (
      conn,
      "localhost",
      "psm",
      "psm1010",
```

```
        "advisory",
      0,
      NULL,
      0);
cgiHeaderContentType("text/html");
fprintf(cgiOut,"<HTML><BODY>");
 fprintf(cgiOut,"Given userid is : %s",username);

 sprintf(query,"select userid from user_id where
userid='%s'",username);
mysql_query(conn,query);
res_set=mysql_store_result(conn);
while((row=mysql_fetch_row(res_set))!=NULL)
{
  for(i=0;i<mysql_num_fields(res_set);i++)  {
strcpy(temp,row[0]);
}   }
mysql_free_result(res_set);
if (strcmp(username,temp)!=0)   {
   mysql_query(conn,"select * from user_id");
   res_set=mysql_store_result(conn);
   sprintf(s1,"insert into user_id set first='%s',
middle='%s', last='%s', village='%s', taluka='%s',
userid='%s'",first,middle,last,
village,taluka,username);
    mysql_query(conn,s1);
   mysql_free_result(res_set);
    flag=1;
   fprintf(cgiOut,"<br><br>Given userid stored in
database.");    }
    else
   {    fprintf(cgiOut,"<br><br>This userid is already
available");
        fprintf(cgiOut,"<br><br><br>");
        fprintf(cgiOut,"<a href=/adv/sign.html>Try
again...</a>");
        fprintf(cgiOut,"<br><br>OR");
     }
       fprintf(cgiOut,"<br><br><a href=/adv/
main.html>Back to main page</a>");
 mysql_close(conn);
conn = mysql_init(NULL);
mysql_real_connect (
     conn,
     "localhost",
```

```
        "psm",
        "psm1010",
          "marathi",
        0,
        NULL,
        0);
if (flag==1)  {
mysql_query(conn,"select * from user_id");
   res_set=mysql_store_result(conn);
   sprintf(s1,"insert into user_id set first='%s',
middle='%s', last='%s', village='%s', taluka='%s',
userid='%s'",first,middle,last,
village,taluka,username);

   mysql_query(conn,s1);
   mysql_free_result(res_set);
    }
fprintf(cgiOut,"</BODY></HTML>");
mysql_close(conn);
free(first);
free(middle);
free(last);
free(village);
free(taluka);
free(username);
free(temp);
free(query);
free(s1);
return 0;
}
```

Section B: To check whether user is normal user or Extension officer or Administrator.

```
# include<stdio.h>
# include "cgic.h"
# include <mysql.h>
# include <string.h>
MYSQL *conn;
MYSQL_RES *res_set;
MYSQL_ROW row;

int cgiMain() {
```

```
char *username,*query,*uid,*pswd,*utype,*temp;
int j,no_of_rows=2 , userflag=0 ,status=0, i=0;

conn = mysql_init(NULL);
mysql_real_connect (
      conn,
      "localhost",
      "psm",
      "psm1010",
        "advisory",
      0,
      NULL,
      0);
username=(char *) malloc(10*sizeof(char));
for(j=0;j<10;j++) {
     username[j]='\0';      }

query=(char *) malloc(200*sizeof(char));
uid=(char *) malloc(10*sizeof(char));
pswd=(char *) malloc(10*sizeof(char));
utype=(char *) malloc(10*sizeof(char));
temp=(char *) malloc(10*sizeof(char));
cgiFormString("username",username,10);
        if ((username[0]==' ')||(username[0]=='\0'))
             {  fprintf(cgiOut,"No name found");
           goto back; }
sprintf(query,"select * from passwd where
userid='%s'",username);
mysql_query(conn,query);
res_set = mysql_store_result(conn);
no_of_rows=mysql_num_rows(res_set);

if (no_of_rows > 1)   {/*mailto*/ }
if (no_of_rows == 0)  {userflag=1; /*That is user is
normal user! */   }
if (no_of_rows == 1)  { userflag=2; /*That is user is EO
*/
                row=mysql_fetch_row(res_set);
                sprintf(pswd,"%s",(char *) row[0]);
                sprintf(uid,"%s",(char *) row[1]);
                sprintf(utype,"%s",(char *) row[2]);
                 }
mysql_free_result(res_set);
cgiHeaderContentType("text/html");
fprintf(cgiOut,"<HTML><BODY>");
```

```
 if
((strcmp(uid,"psm")==0)||(strcmp(uid,"nmt")==0)||(strcmp(uid,"hsa")==0))
goto down;
 if
((strcmp(uid,"ext1")==0)||(strcmp(uid,"ext2")==0)||(strcmp(uid,"ext3")==0))
goto down;
 /* No problem Display Profile , ask question & goto
search*/

/* to check whether userid available in user_id table.
*/
sprintf(query,"select userid from user_id where
userid='%s'",username);
mysql_query(conn,query);
res_set=mysql_store_result(conn);
while((row=mysql_fetch_row(res_set))!=NULL)
{
  for(i=0;i<mysql_num_fields(res_set);i++)  {
strcpy(temp,row[0]);
}   }
mysql_free_result(res_set);

 if (strcmp(username,temp)!=0) {
fprintf(cgiOut,"<br><h3><center>You have not signed-up
earlier.</center></h3><br>");
fprintf(cgiOut,"<br>So please go through the *sign up
here* option on the main page");
fprintf(cgiOut,"<br><br><a href=/adv/main.html>Back to
main page</a>");
   }
   else   status=1;

   if ((userflag==1)&&(status==1)) {
        fprintf(cgiOut, "<CENTER> * * * Welcome %s * * *
<BR><BR>",username);
      sprintf(query,"select * from statistics where
userid='%s'",username);
      mysql_query(conn,query);
      res_set = mysql_store_result(conn);
        fprintf(cgiOut, "<CENTER> Profile<BR><BR>");
        fprintf(cgiOut, "<TABLE ALIGN= \"CENTER\"
Border=\"2\">");
      fprintf(cgiOut,"<TR><TD width=\"15\">Query No</
TD><TD width=\"20\">Posted On</TD><TD
width=\"20\">Solved On</TD></TR>");
```

```
        while((row=mysql_fetch_row(res_set)) != NULL)  {

          if(atoi(row[2])==1) {
          fprintf(cgiOut,"<TR><TD><a
href=dispdel?qid=%s>%s</a></TD>",row[0],row[0]);
          fprintf(cgiOut,"<TD>%s</TD>",row[4]);
          fprintf(cgiOut,"<TD>%s</TD></TR>",row[5]);
          }    }
          fprintf(cgiOut,"</table>");
/* END */
   mysql_free_result(res_set);
   fprintf(cgiOut, "<Form method=post action=search>");
   fprintf(cgiOut, "<BR><BR><pre>    Enter Question:</
pre><BR>");
   fprintf(cgiOut, "<TEXTAREA  rows=\"5\" cols=\"70\"
name=\"qes\"></TEXTAREA>");
   fprintf(cgiOut, "<input type=hidden width=10
name=userid value=\"%s\">",username);
   fprintf(cgiOut, "<BR><BR><input type=submit
name=Submit>  ");
   fprintf(cgiOut, "<input type=reset name=Reset></
form>");
     }      /* if userflag & status == 1 end */
 down:
 if (userflag==2) { /* Seems to be Admin or EO goto ext
page*/
 if(utype[0]=='E') {
   fprintf(cgiOut, "<Form method=post action=ext>");
   fprintf(cgiOut, "Enter Password");
   fprintf(cgiOut, "<input type=password width=10
name=pswd>");
   fprintf(cgiOut, "<input type=hidden width=10
name=apswd value=%s>",pswd);
   fprintf(cgiOut, "<BR><BR><input type=submit
name=Submit>  ");
   fprintf(cgiOut, "<input type=reset name=Reset></
form>");
          }
 if(utype[0]=='A') {
   fprintf(cgiOut, "<Form method=post action=admin>");
   fprintf(cgiOut, "Enter Password");
   fprintf(cgiOut, "<input type=password width=10
name=pswd>");
   fprintf(cgiOut, "<input type=hidden width=10
name=apswd value=%s>",pswd);
```

```
  fprintf(cgiOut, "<BR><BR><input type=submit
name=Submit>  ");
  fprintf(cgiOut, "<input type=reset name=Reset></
form>");
           }
           } /* end of userflag==2 */

goto down2;
back: fprintf(cgiOut,"<br><br><a href=/adv/
main.html>Back to main page</a>");
down2: fprintf(cgiOut,"</BODY></HTML>");
free(username);
free(query);
free(uid);
free(pswd);
free(utype);
free(temp);
return 0;
}
```

Section C: To search the answer for query in database and display it if it is available otherwise redirect it to Extension officer.

```
# include <stdio.h>
#include <string.h>
#include <mysql.h>
# include "cgic.h"

MYSQL *conn;
MYSQL_RES *res_set;
MYSQL_ROW row;
 char
s1[1200],s2[1200],key[50][50],split[50][50],word[50][50],temp[25];
 char
c1,username[10],question[350],answer[800],que[350];
 int x,p,length,i,j,k;

 int cgiMain() {
 int nmt,tqid;
 system("clear");
 conn=mysql_init(NULL);
 mysql_real_connect(
                conn,
```

```
                    "localhost",
                    "psm",
                    "psm1010",
                    "advisory",
                    0,
                    NULL,
                    0 );

 cgiHeaderContentType("text/html");
 for(i=0;i<10;i++)
 { username[i]='\0';  }
for(i=0;i<350;i++)
 { question[i]='\0';  }
 cgiFormString("userid",username,10); ;;
 cgiFormStringNoNewlines("qes",question,350);

 if (question[0] == '\0') {  fprintf(cgiOut,"\nNo
question");
 goto down; }

 fprintf(cgiOut,"<h2>A self upgrading Agricultural
Extension System :<h2><br>");
  length=strlen(question);  length=length+1;
  question[length]=' ';
sprintf(s1,"select max(qid) from statistics");
mysql_query(conn,s1);
res_set=mysql_store_result(conn);
row=mysql_fetch_row(res_set);
mysql_free_result(res_set);
tqid= atoi(row[0]);
tqid=tqid+1;
sprintf(s1,"insert into statistics set
qid=%d,userid='%s'",tqid,username);
mysql_query(conn,s1);

      /* program to read words & compared with question
*/
      j=jval();
      nmt = comp_words(j); /* nmt is 0 means keyword
search +ve */
        /* end of function call */

   if (nmt==0) {
  fprintf(cgiOut,"<form method=post action=addque>");
  fprintf(cgiOut,"<br><br>In database Answer for ur
```

```
question is not available !");
   fprintf(cgiOut,"The question is forwarded to experts,
Next time when u login");
   fprintf(cgiOut,"You may get the answer!<br><br>");
   fprintf(cgiOut,"<input type=hidden name=qid
value=%d>",tqid);
   fprintf(cgiOut,"<input type=hidden name=qes
value=\"%s\">",question);
   fprintf(cgiOut,"<input type=hidden name=ans
value=\"N\">");
   fprintf(cgiOut,"<input type=submit name=Submit>");
   fprintf(cgiOut,"</form>");
    }
    else
    {
   fprintf(cgiOut,"<form method=post action=addque>");
   fprintf(cgiOut,"<br><br>Are you satisfied with above
answer :");
   fprintf(cgiOut,"<input type=hidden name=qid
value=%d>",tqid);
   fprintf(cgiOut,"<input type=hidden name=qes
value=\"%s\">",question);
   fprintf(cgiOut,"<input type=submit name=ans
value=\"N\">");
   fprintf(cgiOut,"<input type=submit name=ans
value=\"Y\">");
   fprintf(cgiOut,"</form>");
    }
   goto back;
down: fprintf(cgiOut,"<br><br><a href=/adv/
main.html>Back to main page</a>");
back: fprintf(cgiOut, "</BODY></HTML>\n");
return 0;
}

int jval() {

/* ****          To generate value of j          **** */
    i=0; j=0;  k=0;
   do
   {
      if (question[i] != ' ')    {
          temp[k]=question[i];
          i++; k++;    }
```

```
        else  {
                  strcpy(split[j],temp);
              i++; j++;  k=0;
                   for(p=0;p<25;p++) { temp[p]='\0'; }
                    }
   }  while(i != length+1);

      /* program to read words & compared with question
*/
       return(j);
       } /* end of jval */
 int comp_words(int j)
{
  int
fl=0,nmt=0,pl=0,i1,j1,k1,len,x,flag=0,kk=0,count=0;
  char cc;
  char ans2[100][850],que2[100][350];
  int lll,rr[25],ctr=0,rpt=0,ll=0;

  mysql_query(conn,"select * from words");
  res_set=mysql_store_result(conn);
  while((row=mysql_fetch_row(res_set)) != NULL)  {
  for(i=0;i<mysql_num_fields(res_set);i++)  {
     strcpy(word[count],row[i]); count++; } }
     mysql_free_result(res_set);
       for(k=0;k<j;k++) {
         for(i=0;i<count;i++)
        {
          x=strcmp(split[k],word[i]);
          if (x==0) { flag=1; goto dn; }
        }
      dn: if (flag==0) { strcpy(key[kk],split[k]);
              kk++;  }
         if (flag==1) flag=0;
        }
      k=0;
      fprintf(cgiOut,"<br>List of Key words generated :
<BR>");
      while(k != kk)  { fprintf(cgiOut,"<br>%s
",key[k]); k++; }

   mysql_query(conn,"select * from faqs");
 res_set=mysql_store_result(conn);
 while((row=mysql_fetch_row(res_set)) != NULL)  {
 for(i=0;i<mysql_num_fields(res_set);i++)  {
```

```
if (i==0) { strcpy(que,row[i]);  i1=0; j1=0; k1=0;
len=strlen(que);  len=len+1;
que[len]=' ';
 do
 {
    if (que[i1] != ' ')    {
        temp[k1]=que[i1];
        i1++; k1++;    }
        else  {
                strcpy(split[j1],temp);
                 i1++; j1++;  k1=0;
                for(p=0;p<25;p++) { temp[p]='\0'; }
                 }
 }  while(i1 != len+1);
 j++;
  } /* i loop completed */

/*  INTRODUCE THE CONCEPT OF SEARCH LEVEL */


 for(k=0;k<kk;k++) {
 for(p1=0;p1<j1;p1++) {
   x=strcmp(key[k],split[p1]);
  if (x==0) { fl=1; goto ans;}          }    }
     ans: if (fl==1)  { if (i==1) {
 strcpy(ans2[ctr],row[i]);
 strcpy(que2[ctr],que); ctr=ctr+1;
                 fl=0; } }
          } /* for loop completed */
      } /* while loop completed */
/*    if (ctr==0) goto no_ans; */
   ctr=ctr-1;
 ll1=ctr;
  while(ctr != -1)
   {
     strcpy(que,que2[ctr]);
     rpt=0; i1=0; j1=0; k1=0;
     len=strlen(que);  len=len+1;
 que[len]=' ';
  do
  {
    if (que[i1] != ' ')    {
        temp[k1]=que[i1];
        i1++; k1++;    }
        else  {
```

```
                    strcpy(split[j1],temp);
                     i1++; j1++;  k1=0;
                     for(p=0;p<25;p++) { temp[p]='\0'; }
                     }
   }  while(i1 != len+1);

  for(k=0;k<kk;k++) {
   for(p1=0;p1<j1;p1++) {
   /* printf("\nPSM %s",split[p1]); */
    x=strcmp(key[k],split[p1]);
     if (x==0) rpt=rpt+1;  }   }
    rr[ctr]=rpt;
     ll=ll+1;
     ctr=ctr-1;
   }
ll=ll-1;

fprintf(cgiOut,"<br>Most likeky answers are :<BR>");
for(i=ll1;i>=0;i–)
{
     if (rr[i]==kk)
          {
                         fprintf(cgiOut,"<table>");
                         fprintf(cgiOut,"<tr>");
                         fprintf(cgiOut,"<th>%s</
th>",ans2[i]);
                         fprintf(cgiOut,"</tr>");
                         fprintf(cgiOut,"</table>");
                          nmt=1;
                        }
  }
  if(nmt==0) fprintf(cgiOut,"Nil<BR>");
  return(nmt);
}
```

Section D: Program to add question and id into the database.

```
# include <stdio.h>
# include <stdlib.h>
# include <string.h>
# include "cgic.h"
# include <mysql.h>
```

```
MYSQL *conn;
MYSQL_RES *res_set;
MYSQL_ROW row;
int cgiMain() {
char *tqid,*ans1,ans,*tque,*s1;
int ttqid=0;
conn = mysql_init(NULL);
mysql_real_connect (
      conn,
      "localhost",
      "psm",
      "psm1010",
      "advisory",
      0,
      NULL,
      0);
      cgiHeaderContentType("text/html");
fprintf(cgiOut,"<HTML><BODY>");
if ((tque=(char *) malloc(1000)) == NULL)
fprintf(cgiOut,"Not enough memory");
memset(tque,' ',999);
memset(tque+999,'\0',1);
if ((tqid=(char *) malloc(5)) == NULL)
fprintf(cgiOut,"Not enough memory");
memset(tqid,' ',4);
memset(tqid+4,'\0',1);
if ((ans1=(char *) malloc(2)) == NULL)
fprintf(cgiOut,"Not enough memory");
memset(ans1,' ',1);
memset(ans1+1,'\0',1);
if ((s1=(char *) malloc(100)) == NULL)
fprintf(cgiOut,"Not enough memory");
memset(s1,' ',99);
memset(s1+99,'\0',1);
cgiFormString("qid",tqid,5);
cgiFormStringNoNewlines("qes",tque,350);
cgiFormString("ans",ans1,2);
ans=ans1[0];

ttqid=atoi(tqid);
if (ans=='N') {
     sprintf(s1,"insert into ans_table set
qid=%d,que='%s'",ttqid,tque);
     mysql_query(conn,s1);
     mysql_free_result(res_set);
```

```
      sprintf(s1,"update statistics set status1='1',
qdate=now() where qid=%d",ttqid);
      mysql_query(conn,s1);
      mysql_free_result(res_set);
            }
            if (ans=='Y') {
      sprintf(s1,"update statistics set status1='0'
qdate=now() , ansdate=now() where qid=%d",ttqid);
      mysql_query(conn,s1);
      mysql_free_result(res_set);
                }

mysql_close(conn);

free(tque);
free(tqid);
free(ans1);
free(s1);
fprintf(cgiOut,"<a href=/adv/main.html>Back</a>");
fprintf(cgiOut,"</HTML></BODY>");
return;
}
```

Section E: Program to check either query pending or solved by expert.

```
# include <stdio.h>
# include "cgic.h"
# include <mysql.h>
# include <string.h>
# include <stdlib.h>
MYSQL *conn;
MYSQL_RES *res_set;
MYSQL_ROW row;

int cgiMain() {
char *iqid,*s1;
int id,i;
cgiHeaderContentType("text/html");
if ((iqid=(char *) malloc(6)) == NULL)
fprintf(cgiOut,"Not enough memory");
memset(iqid,' ',5);
memset(iqid+5,'\0',1);
if ((s1=(char *) malloc(200)) == NULL)
```

```
fprintf(cgiOut,"Not enough memory");
memset(s1,' ',199);
memset(s1+199,'\0',1);
cgiFormString("qid",iqid,6);
conn = mysql_init(NULL);
mysql_real_connect (
      conn,
      "localhost",
      "psm",
      "psm1010",
      "advisory",
      0,
      NULL,
      0);

fprintf(cgiOut,"<HTML><BODY>");
 id=atoi(iqid);

  sprintf(s1,"select * from faqs where qid=%d",id);
  mysql_query(conn,s1);
  res_set=mysql_store_result(conn);
  i=mysql_num_rows(res_set);
    if(i==0) {
  fprintf(cgiOut,"<BR><Br>Answer of your query is yet
NOT available <BR><BR>");
    }
  if(i==1) {
   while((row=mysql_fetch_row(res_set)) != NULL)
   {
    for(i=0;i<mysql_num_fields(res_set);i++)
     {
  fprintf(cgiOut,"<table><tr><th> %s</th></tr></
table>",row[i]);
    } }
          }
fprintf(cgiOut,"<a href=/adv/main.html>Back to main
page...</a>");
fprintf(cgiOut,"</BODY></HTML>");
mysql_free_result(res_set);
free(iqid);
free(s1);
return 0;
}
```

Section F: Program to update query and answer into a table.

```
#include <stdio.h>
#include <string.h>
#include <stdlib.h>
#include <mysql.h>
#include "cgic.h"
MYSQL *conn;
MYSQL_RES *res_set;
MYSQL_ROW row;

 int cgiMain()
  {
 int id2,i,id,q1=0;
 char *s1,*s2,*s3;
 char *idd,*question,*answer;
 conn=mysql_init(NULL);
 mysql_real_connect(
                conn,
                "localhost",
                "psm",
                "psm1010",
                "advisory",
                0,
                NULL,
                0 );
   cgiHeaderContentType("text/html");
  fprintf(cgiOut,"<HTML><BODY><br>");
if ((idd=(char *) malloc(5)) == NULL)
fprintf(cgiOut,"Not enough memory");
memset(idd,' ',4);
memset(idd+4,'\0',1);
if ((question=(char *) malloc(400)) == NULL)
fprintf(cgiOut,"Not enough memory");
memset(question,' ',399);
memset(question+399,'\0',1);
if ((answer=(char *) malloc(1200)) == NULL)
fprintf(cgiOut,"Not enough memory");
memset(answer,' ',1199);
memset(answer+1199,'\0',1);
if ((s1=(char *) malloc(2000)) == NULL)
fprintf(cgiOut,"Not enough memory");
memset(s1,' ',1999);
memset(s1+1999,'\0',1);
```

```
if ((s2=(char *) malloc(200)) == NULL)
fprintf(cgiOut,"Not enough memory");
memset(s2,' ',199);
memset(s2+199,'\0',1);
if ((s3=(char *) malloc(200)) == NULL)
fprintf(cgiOut,"Not enough memory");
memset(s3,' ',199);
memset(s3+199,'\0',1);

  cgiFormString("id",idd,5);
  cgiFormStringNoNewlines("ans1",answer,1199);
   id2=atoi(idd);

  sprintf(s1,"select que from ans_table where
qid=%d",id2);
  mysql_query(conn,s1);
  res_set=mysql_store_result(conn);
  while ((row=mysql_fetch_row(res_set)) != NULL)
  {   for(i=0;i<mysql_num_fields(res_set);i++)
      {  strcpy(question,row[i]);     }       }
    fprintf(cgiOut,"Que=%s",question);
  mysql_free_result(res_set);
     mysql_query(conn,"select * from faqs");
  res_set=mysql_store_result(conn);
  sprintf(s1,"insert into faqs set question='%s' ,
answer='%s' ,qid=%d",question,answer,id2);
  sprintf(s2,"delete from ans_table where qid=%d",id2);
  sprintf(s3,"update statistics set status2='0' ,
ansdate=now() where qid=%d",id2);
  mysql_query(conn,s1);
  mysql_query(conn,s2);
  mysql_query(conn,s3);
  mysql_free_result(res_set);
  fprintf(cgiOut,"<a href=/adv/main.html>Back to main
page</a>");
  fprintf(cgiOut,"</BODY></HTML>");
  mysql_close(conn);
   free(idd);
   free(question);
   free(answer);
   free(s1);
   free(s2);
   free(s3);
   return ;
}
```

Section G: Program to provide answer for the queries, which are pending.

```
#include <stdio.h>
#include <string.h>
#include <stdlib.h>
#include <mysql.h>
#include "cgic.h"
MYSQL *conn;
MYSQL_RES *res_set;
MYSQL_ROW row;
  int cgiMain()
 {
 char *q[350];
 char *ans1,*pswd,*apswd;
 int i,q1=0,id,id1[200];
 conn=mysql_init(NULL);
 mysql_real_connect(
                  conn,
                  "localhost",
                  "psm",
                  "psm1010",
                  "advisory",
                  0,
                  NULL,
                  0 );
  cgiHeaderContentType("text/html");
  fprintf(cgiOut,"<HTML><BODY><br>");
for(i=0;i<100;i++)
{ q[i] = (char *) malloc(350*sizeof(char)); }

if ((pswd=(char *) malloc(10)) == NULL)
fprintf(cgiOut,"Not enough memory");

if ((apswd=(char *) malloc(10)) == NULL)
fprintf(cgiOut,"Not enough memory");

if ((ans1=(char *) malloc(1200)) == NULL)
fprintf(cgiOut,"Not enough memory");

  cgiFormString("pswd",pswd,10);
  cgiFormString("apswd",apswd,10);
  if(strcmp(pswd,apswd)!=0) {
     fprintf(cgiOut,"Invalid Password Try Again</
HTML></BODY>");
```

```
        fprintf(cgiOut,"<BR><BR><a href=/adv/
main.html>Back to main page</a>");
        fprintf(cgiOut,"</BODY></HTML>");
         return;       }
   mysql_query(conn,"select * from ans_table");
   res_set=mysql_store_result(conn);
   while((row=mysql_fetch_row(res_set)) != NULL)  {
   for(i=0;i<mysql_num_fields(res_set);i++)  {
       if (i==0) {  id1[q1]=atoi(row[0]);
fprintf(cgiOut,"<br>Qid=%s  ",row[0]); }
       if (i==1)  { strcpy(q[q1],row[1]);
              fprintf(cgiOut,"Que=%s",q[q1]);
               q1++;  }
     }
    fprintf(cgiOut,"<br>"); }
    mysql_free_result(res_set);
   fprintf(cgiOut,"<form method=post action=updat>");
   fprintf(cgiOut,"<br>Enter the qid for which providing
a answer :");
   fprintf(cgiOut, "<input type=text name=id
value=%d>",id);
   fprintf(cgiOut, "<pre>Enter Answer :<BR><BR></pre>");
   fprintf(cgiOut, "<TEXTAREA  rows=\"11\" cols=\"70\"
name=\"ans1\"></TEXTAREA>");
   fprintf(cgiOut,"<input type=submit name=Submit>");
   fprintf(cgiOut, "</Form>");
   fprintf(cgiOut,"</BODY></HTML>");
   mysql_close(conn);
    free(pswd);
    free(apswd);
    free(ans1);
    for(i=0;i<100;i++)  {  free(q[i]);  }
}
```

Section H: Program to display the statistics of Query solved by: Advisory system or Extension officer or still unsolved.

```
#include <stdio.h>
#include <string.h>
#include <stdlib.h>
#include <mysql.h>
#include "cgic.h"
MYSQL *conn;
```

```
MYSQL_RES *res_set;
MYSQL_ROW row;

  int cgiMain()
  {
   int i,rec;
  char *pswd,*apswd,*s1;
  conn=mysql_init(NULL);
  mysql_real_connect(
                    conn,
                    "localhost",
                    "psm",
                    "psm1010",
                    "advisory",
                    0,
                    NULL,
                    0 );
   cgiHeaderContentType("text/html");
   fprintf(cgiOut,"<HTML><BODY><br>");
 if ((pswd=(char *) malloc(10)) == NULL)
 fprintf(cgiOut,"Not enough memory");
 memset(pswd,' ',9);
 memset(pswd+9,'\0',1);
  if ((apswd=(char *) malloc(10)) == NULL)
 fprintf(cgiOut,"Not enough memory");
 memset(apswd,' ',9);
 memset(apswd+9,'\0',1);
  if ((s1=(char *) malloc(250)) == NULL)
 fprintf(cgiOut,"Not enough memory");
 memset(s1,' ',249);
 memset(s1+249,'\0',1);
   cgiFormString("pswd",pswd,10);
   cgiFormString("apswd",apswd,10);
   if(strcmp(pswd,apswd)!=0) {
      fprintf(cgiOut,"Invalid Password Try Again</
HTML></BODY>");
   fprintf(cgiOut,"<BR><BR><a href=/adv/main.html>Back
to main page</a>");
   fprintf(cgiOut,"</BODY></HTML>");
                             }
else {
      fprintf(cgiOut,"<center><h3>Administrator
Profile</h3><br>");
      fprintf(cgiOut,"<center><h4>Question solved by</
h4><br>");
```

```
      fprintf(cgiOut,"<Table Align=\"center\"
Border=\"2\">");
      fprintf(cgiOut,"<TR><TD width=\"25\">Advisory
system
                              </TD><TD width=\"25\">Extension
Officer
                              </TD><TD width=\"25\">still
unsolved
      </TD></TR>");
      sprintf(s1,"select count(*) from statistics where
status1='0' and status2 not in ('0')");
      mysql_query(conn,s1);
      res_set=mysql_store_result(conn);
      while((row=mysql_fetch_row(res_set)) != NULL)
         {
        for(i=0;i<mysql_num_fields(res_set);i++)
         {
        fprintf(cgiOut,"<TD>%s</TD>",row[i]);  } }
      mysql_free_result(res_set);

      sprintf(s1,"select count(*) from statistics where
status1='1' and status2='0'");
      mysql_query(conn,s1);
      res_set=mysql_store_result(conn);
        while((row=mysql_fetch_row(res_set)) != NULL)
         {
        for(i=0;i<mysql_num_fields(res_set);i++)
         {
        fprintf(cgiOut,"<TD>%s</TD>",row[i]);  } }

      mysql_free_result(res_set);

      sprintf(s1,"select count(*) from statistics where
status1='1' and status2 not in ('0')");
      mysql_query(conn,s1);
      res_set=mysql_store_result(conn);
      while((row=mysql_fetch_row(res_set)) != NULL)
         {
for(i=0;i<mysql_num_fields(res_set);i++)
         {           fprintf(cgiOut,"<TD>%s</
TD><br>",row[i]);  } }
      mysql_free_result(res_set);
      free(pswd);
      free(apswd);
      free(s1);
```

```
    fprintf(cgiOut,"</table>");
    fprintf(cgiOut,"</HTML></BODY>");
      fprintf(cgiOut,"<BR><BR><a href=/adv/
main.html>Back to main page</a>");
      fprintf(cgiOut,"</BODY></HTML>");        }    }
```

Appendix 2

Sixty-four states and Stability of the crop

Serial No.	States of the markets (Bipolar signal)						Number of weeks required for the state becomes stable			
							Jawar	Wheat	Tur	Mug
1	1	1	1	1	1	1	2	2	1	1
2	-1	1	1	1	1	1	2	2	2	2
3	1	-1	1	1	1	1	2	2	2	2
4	-1	-1	1	1	1	1	2	2	2	2
5	1	1	-1	1	1	1	2	2	2	2
6	-1	1	-1	1	1	1	2	2	2	2
7	1	-1	-1	1	1	1	2	2	3	2
8	-1	-1	-1	1	1	1	2	1	3	2
9	1	1	1	-1	1	1	2	2	2	2
10	1	1	1	1	-1	1	2	2	1	2
11	1	-1	1	-1	1	1	2	2	2	2
12	-1	-1	1	-1	1	1	2	2	2	2
13	1	1	-1	-1	1	1	2	2	2	2
14	-1	1	-1	-1	1	1	2	2	2	2
15	1	-1	-1	-1	1	1	2	1	2	2
16	-1	-1	-1	-1	1	1	2	2	3	2
17	1	1	1	1	-1	1	2	2	2	2
18	-1	1	1	1	-1	1	2	2	2	2
19	1	-1	1	1	-1	1	2	2	2	2
20	-1	-1	1	1	-1	1	2	2	3	2
21	1	1	-1	1	-1	1	2	2	2	2
22	-1	1	-1	1	-1	1	2	2	3	2
23	1	-1	-1	1	-1	1	2	2	2	3
24	-1	-1	-1	1	-1	1	2	1	2	2
25	1	1	1	-1	-1	1	2	2	2	2
26	-1	1	1	-1	-1	1	2	2	2	3
27	1	-1	1	-1	-1	1	2	2	3	2
28	-1	-1	1	-1	-1	1	2	2	2	2

Serial No.	States of the markets (Bipolar signal)						Number of weeks required for the state becomes stable			
							Jawar	Wheat	Tur	Mug
29	1	1	-1	-1	-1	1	2	2	3	2
30	-1	1	-1	-1	-1	1	2	2	2	2
31	1	-1	-1	-1	-1	1	2	2	2	2
32	-1	-1	-1	-1	-1	1	1	2	3	2
33	1	1	1	1	1	-1	1	2	2	2
34	-1	1	1	1	1	-1	2	2	2	2
35	1	-1	1	1	1	-1	2	2	2	2
36	-1	-1	1	1	1	-1	2	2	3	2
37	1	1	-1	1	1	-1	2	2	2	2
38	-1	1	-1	1	1	-1	2	2	3	2
39	1	-1	-1	1	1	-1	2	2	2	3
40	-1	-1	-1	1	1	-1	2	2	2	2
41	1	1	1	-1	1	-1	2	1	1	2
42	-1	1	1	-1	1	-1	2	2	3	3
43	1	-1	1	-1	1	-1	2	2	4	2
44	-1	-1	1	-1	1	-1	2	2	4	2
45	1	1	-1	-1	1	-1	2	2	4	2
46	-1	1	-1	-1	1	-1	2	2	4	2
47	1	-1	-1	-1	1	-1	2	2	2	2
48	-1	-1	-1	-1	1	-1	2	2	3	2
49	1	1	1	1	-1	-1	2	2	2	2
50	-1	1	1	1	-1	-1	2	1	2	2
51	1	-1	1	1	-1	-1	2	2	2	2
52	-1	-1	1	1	-1	-1	2	2	2	2
53	1	1	-1	1	-1	-1	2	2	2	2
54	-1	1	-1	1	-1	-1	2	2	2	2
55	1	-1	-1	1	-1	-1	2	2	1	2
56	-1	-1	-1	1	-1	-1	2	2	2	2
57	1	1	1	-1	-1	-1	2	1	2	2
58	-1	1	1	-1	-1	-1	2	2	3	2
59	1	-1	1	-1	-1	-1	2	2	2	2
60	-1	-1	1	-1	-1	-1	2	2	3	2
61	1	1	-1	-1	-1	-1	2	2	2	2
62	-1	1	-1	-1	-1	-1	2	2	3	2
63	1	-1	-1	-1	-1	-1	2	2	2	2
64	-1	-1	-1	-1	-1	-1	2	2	2	1

Definitions:

Farmer or Producer: - Producer who produces grain and cotton.

Marketiers: - The people who are doing business related to agricultural inputs.

Extension Worker (T&V): - The workers who receive information from various available sources and given to farmer for better farming, this process is called Training and Visit system.

Agro Processor: - People who process or runs oil mill, dal mill, floor mill, sawmill etc.

Financier: - Bank peoples who provides loans, subsidies etc on agricultural inputs and farming.

Research Worker: - The person who collects information from farmers, extension workers and existing available literature then processes it and generate a new information and disseminate it.

FAQ's: - The question that comes to mind often frequently is called frequently asked questions.

HowTo: - which give detail description of any problem or sub problem.

Main Marker Committee (MMC): - It deals with auction of Grain market via commission agent.

(Sub Marker Committee) SMC: - It is a sub market of MMC that deals only with cotton market.

Data structure: - Mathematical or logical organization of data is called data structure.

APMC organizational people: - The employee who are working under market committee are called APMC organizational people.

Commission Agent: - CA is a person who takes care of goods until auction and charges a commission on it to producer.

Wholesaler or Trader: - Wholesaler is a goods purchaser from CA and must be a license holder of Market committee.

Acronyms

A

AIS: Agro Information System

APMC: Agricultural Produce Market Committee.

A.R.: Assistant Registrar.

AEO: Agriculture Extension Officer

ARPIS: Agricultural Research Personnel Information System.

ARFIS: Agricultural Research Financial Information System.

ARIS: Agricultural Research Information System.

AIR: All India Radio

ATIC: Agricultural Technology Information Center.

API: Application Programming Interface.

B

BSNL: Bharat Sanchar Nigam Limited

BAM: Bi-directional Associative Memory

DBI: Data Base Interface.

DBD: Database Driver.

C

CA: Commission Agent.

C.S: Co-operative Society.

CGI: Common Gateway Interface.

CISC: Complex Instruction Set Computer.

D

DFD: Data Flow Diagram.

D.D.R.: District Deputy Registrar.

DSMS: District Subject Matter Specialist

DJR (cs): Divisional Joint Registrar.

DBMS: Database Management System.

E

EP: Extension Personnel

F

FAQ: Frequently Asked Question.

G

GIS: Geographical Information System

H

HTML: Hyper Text Markup Language.

I

IS: Information System

ISP: Internet Service Provider

IT: Information Technology

IDU: Indoor Unit

ICAR: Indian Council of Agricultural Research

J

JDA = Joint Director of Agriculture

K

KVK: Krishi Vidyan Kendra

L

LAN: Local Area Network

M

MIS: Management Information System.

MMC: Main Market Committee.

M.S.A.M.B.: Maharashtra State Agricultural Marketing Board.

MIB: Market Intelligence Branch.

MRO: Marketing Research Officer.

MQ: Messaging Queue.

M.A.U.: Marathwada Agricultural University.

N

NGO: Non - Government Organization

NBSS&LUP: National Bureau of Soil Survey & Land Use Planning

NARS: National Agricultural Research System.

O

OR: Operation Research.

P

PAO : Principal Agriculture Officer

PHP: Personal Home Page.

R

RISC: Reduced Instruction Set Computer.

RDBMS: Relational Data Base Management System.

S

SDA: State Department of Agriculture

SDI: State Department of Irrigation

SMC: Sub Market Committee.

SDEO: Sub-Divisional Extension Officer

SMS: Subject Matter Specialist

SAU: State Agricultural Universities.

SMP: Symmetric Multiprocessing.

T

T&V: Training and Visit System

TTF: True Type font

V

VSAT: Very Small Aperture Terminal

VEW: Village Extension Worker

VAIS: Virtual Agro Information System.

VS: Voice Recognition

VPNS: Virtual Private Network Service.

W

WCG: Warana Group of Co-operatives

WAN: Wide Area Network

WSS: Warana Sahakari Sangh

WORM: Write Once Read Many.

Z

ZEO : Zonal Extension Officer.

References

Aher A.J. (1999). 'A study on effectiveness of farm broadcast of All India Radio, Mumbai'.M.Sc. (Agri.) Thesis, Konkan Krishi Vidyapeeth, Dapoli.

All India Radio (2000).

Awad E.M.(1998), System Analysis and Design Publ: Galgotia Publications Pvt. Ltd., Delhi-2

Alam (2001), Agro Informatics., pp 1-4, INSAIT Dharwad.

Alex Berson (1992), Client / Server Architecture, publ McGraw-Hill series on Computer Communications.

Bellurkar C.M. (1990). Study on the impact of Television programmes with special reference to Agriculture and Home science technology. Department of Extension Education , M.A.U. Parbhani. (M.S.)

Bhosle P.B. (2000). Study on effectiveness of farm broadcast of All India Radio. Department of Extension Education , M.A.U. Parbhani. (M.S.)

Bigelow(2000), Troubleshooting, Maintaining, & Repairing PCs. Tata McGraw-Hill.

Baliraja Magazine (Jan 98, Oct 97, Dec 97, Nov 98, June 98, July 98, sept 98 and Apr 98).

Bank directory, (1997 - 98), Suneja publishers, New Delhi.

Chambhargekar D.R. (2001). Survey report on Radio station Parbhani. Dissertation submitted to Institute of Information Technology and Management, Parbhani 431 401 (M.S.) India.

Chandel C.G. (1980) Economic Analysis of Market arrivals and prices of Principle crops in Parbhani Dist., Dissertation submitted to the Dept of Economics., Marathwada Agricultural University, Parbhani for MSc Degree.

Computer Communication (May 1997), ADIT, CDAC, Pune.

Dikle R.N. (1990). Role of Newspaper in communication of Agricultural information. Department of Extension Education, M.A.U. Parbhani. (M.S.)

Digraskar,R.K.(1996).Communication behavior in farm innovation development ,extension and client systems of Marathwada region in Maharashtra state : A system approach. Department of Extension Education,M.A.U. Parbhani (M.S)

Davis and Olson (1984), Management Information Systems: conceptual foundations, structure and development.

Goyal G., Roy S. and Veerpal K. (1998). Journal of Research, Punjab Agril. Univ 35(1-2) : 112-114, May / June 1998.

Hunter G. (1970). The administration of Agricultural development. Lessons from India. Oxford University Press, New York.

Heywood, Cornelius and Carver (2000), An Introduction to GISs.

Kubde V.R. and Choudhari V.D. (1992). Television viewers from rural areas and their opinion about the rural telecast. Maha. Jr. of extn. Edn., XI : 179-181.

Kasle, P.V. (1998) Study of agro - processing industries in Maharashtra State . Department of Agril.Economics,M.A.U. Parbhani (M.S.)

Kosko B .,(2000), Neural Networks and Fuzzy Systems - A dynamical systems approach to Machine intelligence, PHI Pvt Ltd., New Delhi

Lionberger H.F. and Chang C. (1970). Flow of farm information for modernizing agriculture : The Taiwan system. Praeger publishers, New York.

Mogal S.W. (1989) Price structure of Onion in Maharashtra, Dissertation submitted to Dept of Economics ., Marathwada Agricultural University, Parbhani for MSc Degree.

Maji A.K., and Krishna N.D.R (1996) Application of Geographical Information System in Soil Resource Management, Agropedology, 6:75-78.

Maji A. K., Krishna N.D.R , Sehagal J., and Velayutham M (1998), Dissimination of Soil Information for District Level Planning Using GIS. GIS India . 7:21-25

Mook (2001), Agro Informatics., pp 5-8, INSAIT Dharwad.

Mane R.S. (1988). Study of usefulness of community Television sets with special reference to Agriculture development. Department of Extension Education , M.A.U. Parbhani. (M.S.)

Novak J.L. and Stegelin F.E. (1988), U.S. Farmer's attitudes towards microcomputer uses. Comput Electron.Agric.,3:81-89.

Naber G., (1994), Land drainage: Bibliography and Information retrieval.

National Bureau of Soil Survey & Land Use Planning (1997), Agricultural division, State Govt. Pune, NBSS publ 54.

Obi Reddy, G.P., Maji A. K., Srinivas C.V., Kamble K. H., and

Velayutham, M. (2001), Proceeding of the first National Conf on Agro-Informatics, Dharwad, p34 - 39.

Prakash, V. and Venkatramani G.,(2000). Role for Informatics, The Hindu Survey of Indian Agriculture 2000.

Parbhani television station (2000).

Patil C.B. (2000). Study on effectiveness of farm telecast on Doordarshan. Department of Extension Education , M.A.U. Parbhani. (M.S.)

Pokale, S.N.(1994). A study of parbhani (APMC) regulated market. Department of Agril. Economics, M.A.U. Parbhani. (M.S.)

Pratiksha Computer Centre (2002), Parbhani

Pokale S.N., (1994), Study of Parbhani (APMC) Regulated Market., Dissertation submitted to Dept. of Economics ., Marathwada Agricultural University, Parbhani for MSc Degree.

Rosaiah, Y., and Palanisamy, A (2001), Community teleservice Centres a tool for rural development, Proceeding of the first National Conf on Agro-Informatics, Dharwad, p80 - 83.

Rao N.R. (1991). Television viewing behaviour of farmers in Marathwada region. Department of Extension Education, M.A.U. Parbhani. (M.S.)

Rajora and Vyas (March 2001). "Gyandoot" by Zilla Panchayat, Dhar MP won the CSI - TCS, CSI Communications.

Saxena A.K., Thakur P. and Shrivastava A. (1995). Utility of farm information dissemination through radio and television. Maha . Jr. of Extn. Edn., XIV : 65-68.

Sandhu A.S. (1973). 'Credibility of radio as a source of farm information'. Research journal. 10 (2) : 234-237.

Suryawanshi C.M. (1992). Study on Assessment or Training needs or contact farmers in Training and Visit system. Department of Extension Education , M.A.U. Parbhani. (M.S.)

Satpute T.G. (1985). Study of water allocation in the command area of Jayakwadi irrigation project , Maharashtra. Department of Agril. Economics, M.A.U. Parbhani. (M.S.)

Statistical abstract of M.S.(2000), Directorate of Economics & Statistics, Govt. of Maharashtra, Mumbai.

Sonawane P.P. (2000). Study on Newspaper reading behaviour of farmers. Department of Extension Education , M.A.U. Parbhani. (M.S.)

Sirsat U.E. (1982), Study of effectiveness of University publication Sheti-Bhati. Department of Extension Education , M.A.U. Parbhani. (M.S.)

Thombre, B.M. (1979). Mass media of communication in disseminating farm information - A comparative analysis.Department of Extension Education , M.A.U. Parbhani. (M.S.)

Tanenbaum (2001), Computer network.

T. Balaguru., P. manikandan and C. Kalla (1996), Management Information System for Agricultural Research.

Venkaratnam L. (2001) Remote sensing and GIS applications in Agriculture, (2001) , Proceeding of the first National Conf on Agro-Informatics, Dharwad, p20-29.

Vedapathak, H.P.(1997). Impact of T and V system on technological and behavioral changes among the contact farmers. Department of Extension education, M.A.U. Parbhani.(M.S.)

Waterman (1986), A guide to Expert Systems.

http://www.alw.nih.gov/security/prog_firewall.htm

http://www.mdnsweb1.mdns.att.com/att/att_tech_center4.html

http://www.eecs.wsu.edu/~bakken/middleware-article-bakken.pdf

http://www.fastwebsites.co.uk/portvscorp.htm

http://www.user.dtcc.edu/~berlin/font/indian.htm

http://www.intel.com/design/servers/buildingblocks/board.htm

http://www.education.hp.com/datasheets/U4167S.pdf

http://www.raitamitra.kar.nic.in

http://www.nic.in/icar

http://www.exportersindia.net/fertilizers.htm

http://www.icar.org.in

http://www.agriculture.com

http://www.accuspray.com

http://www.fertindia.com

http://www.fadinap.org

http://www.uttamkrishi.com

http://www.foodtrader.com

http://www.agriwatch.com

http://www.agmachine-india.com

http://www.agroservice.hu

http://www.undp.org

http://www.engfarmchina.com

http://www.indiaagronet.com

http://www.farmers.com

http://www.powerfarm.com

http://www.indianagriculture.com

http://www.industrialtradefair.com

http://www.agriintex.com

http://www.khetibadi.com

http://www.ekrishimitra.com

http://www.kisan.com

http://www.mercindia.com/otherlinks.htm

http://www.artsact.com/technical.htm

http://www.trah.com/leased-lines.htm

http://whatis.techtarget.com/definition/0,289893,sid9_gci213004,00.html

http://msdn.microsoft.com/library/default.asp?url=/library/enus/off2000/html/defUnicode.asp

http://www.marketonline.com

http://www.ams.usda.gov

http://www.agmrc.org

http://www.nama.org

http://www.statpub.com

http://www.agriculture.com

http://www.aec.msu.edu/agecon/fs2/market_information.htm

http://www.agrimark.com

http://www.cimis.water.ca.gov

http://forages.orst.edu/IS/AIS/enfpmain.cfm?PageID

http://www.cm.ksc.co.th/~bruns/9_info.html

http://www.fao.org/ag/agl/aglw/aquastat/regions/lac/index5.stm

http://www.vl-irrigation.org/cms/index.php?id=137

http://www.worc.ac.uk/services/equalopps/VRproject/voicerec.htm

http://members.tripod.com/~TKIET_SHIT_Group/

http://www.cpuscorecard.com/arch_news.htm

http://www.artsact.com/technical.htm

www.genomicglossaries.com/content/chemoinformatics_gloss.asp

http://techlibrary.internetweek.com/data/detail?id=1023823300_72&type=RES

http://www.geocities.com/hstein98/Approx.htm

http://www.cix.co.uk/~smctighe/Files/ASRC%20Observers%20Guide.doc

Index

A

Agricultural colleges 38
Agricultural Marketing Subsystem 119
Agricultural Technology Information Centre 35
Agro Information System 61
AIS 64
APMC organization module 131
Artificial Neural Network 138

B

BSNL stations 30
Business rules 127

C

Chat session establishment 79
CISC 80
Commission Agent module 127
communication channel 62
Communication services 82
Connection of VSAT 71

D

Data Mining Concepts 54
Data Warehousing Strategies 147
Database access 82
Design specifications 67
Direct communication 35
dissemination of Information 27
Doordarshan 28
dynamic pages 96

E

E - Finance tools 79
E-auction 127
Electronic media 27
Evaluation of Doordarshan 15
Evaluation of Radio 15
Expert System on Irrigation 151

F

Facsimile services 82
Farm - Advisory Subsystem 93
farm journals 36
Farmer module 126
Fertilizer Industries 45
File sharing 81
Firewall softwares 75

G

GIS software 78

H

Humanware 67

I

Indian language processing capabilities 114
Informants 23
information flow diagrams 52
Information Generation 37
Information System 61
Information Technology 17
Interfacing techniques 89
Internet 30
Irrigation related websites 146
Irrigation Subsystem 145

L

Leased line 83
Leased line connection 71
Literature Survey 3

M

Mail tools 79

Middleware concepts 88
Multi-user support 82
Multilingual requirements 85
Multimedia 82

N

Networking 82

P

Pesticide and Insecticide industries 46
Print media 36
Printer sharing 81
Problem Identification 9
Production Mechanisms 37
Programme production 55

R

Radio 27
Regulated Market System 136
Relational Database Management System 102
RISC 80

S

Scalability 82
Search Engines 78
Secondary Data 23
Seed agencies 39
Seed industries 44
Selecting fonts 86
Self Upgrading Advisory Tool 101
Server hardware architecture 79
Simulators 78
Smart card technology 84
Statistical Tools 78
Survey 22
Symmetric Multiprocessing 80
System Analysis 21

T

telecasting 55
Tools room 77
Traders module 130
Trend Estimators 78
Trend Generators 78

U

Unicode technology 85
User requirement tools 78

V

V-SAT Numbers 47
Videoconferencing facility 79
Virtual Agro Information System 21
Virtual Classrooms 162
Virtual Lab 163
Virtual Library 160
Virtual Private Network technology 87
Virtual University 161
Voice Recognition Software 117

W

weather and soils 47
Web enabled services 160
Web enabled Simulated Experiment 163
Website of ICAR organizations 154